"Hawthorne Writes is a good example of how our teachers are inspiring young students to reach for their dreams."

Mike Neill
Superintendent of Schools
Ottawa-Carleton District School Board

"Hawthorne Writes is a wonderful initiative by two of our staff, Michael Fuchigami and Susan Newton, to showcase the talent and writing enthusiasm of our students. As a diverse and dynamic school, we believe that every student can succeed in being a good writer. Each story was translated into a different language representing the students' cultural heritage and family roots. This is one of our greatest strengths as a school...that we are a window to the world!"

Francesse Kopczewski
Principal, Hawthorne PS

"Hawthorne Writes has been exciting and challenging. At Hawthorne, we are working with students and families with tremendous potential; who can learn from us; and more importantly who have a lot to teach us when we give them the voice and the tools that they need to participate as equal partners in education."

Susan Newton
Junior Kindergarten Teacher

"From the story of one child, to a classroom, to a school, to a community, to a city, to a country, to around the world – what a wonderful way to hear our children's voices."

Sharron Mahon
Co-Chair Hawthorne School Council

"I like how you get to see a side of everyone – something you didn't know before. Everyone is different in their own way and we've had the opportunity to see it and express it in our writing."

Urge Ibrahim
Grade 8 Student; Student Council Co-President

"I have been at Hawthorne for eight years and I have never been a part of anything like this. Hawthorne Writes is a school project, which shows everyone how diverse Hawthorne Public School is. It has given me a great chance to practise my mother tongue, read stories from people who come from all over the world and enjoy myself by translating stories into Serbo-Croatian."

Djordje Djuric
Grade 8 Student

Hawthorne *Writes*
because everyone has a story...

**70 Stories from Students and Staff
to Share Similarities
and Celebrate Differences**

MIKE FUCHIGAMI (EDITOR IN CHIEF)
SUSAN NEWTON
FRANCESSE KOPCZEWSKI

Amy Schaefer
Karen Skelly
Stephanie Ettinger
Terry Plumb

Students and Staff of Hawthorne Public School

OTTAWA-CARLETON
DISTRICT SCHOOL BOARD

Read our stories online at:
www1.ocdsb.ca/HawtWeb/HawthorneWrites

May those who live in the shadows
Be seen by those in the sun

John Marsden
Prayer for the 21st Century

About Hawthorne Public School

Hawthorne Public School is an elementary school located in Ottawa, Canada. We have nearly 500 students from Kindergarten to Grade Eight speaking 40 different languages and representing over 50 countries of origin. At Hawthorne, one is always surrounded by children and adults who reflect the international reality of our city and country. As such, recognizing our diversity and teaching anti-racism and equity education is a necessity. For more information about us, please contact the school directly.

Hawthorne Public School
Principal: F. Kopczewski • Vice Principal: R. Little

2158 St. Laurent Blvd.• Ottawa, Ontario, Canada • K1G 1A9
Phone: 613-733-6221 • Fax: 613-521-1765

Acknowledgements and Permissions
Permissions are included at the back. Although we have made efforts to properly credit all of the individuals involved in Hawthorne Writes, due to the magnitude of the project and the print deadline required to publish during the school year, some errors and omissions may have occurred. If you notice any errors or inaccuracies, please visit our website or email us at hawthorneps@ocdsb.ca so we can correct our online version, as well as make corrections in future printings of this book.

Cover Photo Credit
© 2006 Richard Smith, Teacher
www.metrophotography.ca

ISBN 0-9781180-0-6

First Printing: June 2006
Printed in Ottawa, Canada

Table of Contents

ix

x

Acknowledgements

Hawthorne Writes took eight months and many hours of hard work, to go from an idea to a published book. It has been a whole school initiative supported by parents and the Ottawa Carleton District School Board educational community. But first and foremost, we must gratefully thank Michael Fuchigami for his creative vision in coming up with this project. It is because of his idea and his determination to see this through to a successful end that Hawthorne Writes has become a reality. His energy and enthusiasm for all aspects of production through these many months has been nothing short of awe-inspiring to his colleagues and students and we are sure that when our students pick up their book in years to come, they will always send a silent message of gratitude to this dedicated teacher. Secondly, we must thank Susan Newton, who early on in the planning stages brought substance to the idea through her data-based research into the cultures and languages in our school and her understanding of the importance of first language literacy in the success of our students. Her tireless work with staff and students provided the foundation upon which the book was built. Our principal, Francesse Kopczewski has been entirely supportive and encouraging. A project of this magnitude would never have been possible if she had not believed in her staff and allowed them to take risks to see this initiative to its conclusion, this first edition of 'Hawthorne Writes'. For this and for the countless other contributions she has made on behalf of Hawthorne staff, families, and students we thank her.

At the school board level we would like to acknowledge Ottawa Carleton District School Board Director, Dr. Lorne Rachlis and Superintendent Mike Neill. Without their support this would not have been possible. Thanks to Sharlene Hunter, Maggie Melenhorst and Hyacinth Haddad from the Communications department for their support with media. Special thanks to Debasree Banerji, Educational Officer, International Languages Program, her teaching staff and students for translating our children's stories into their heritage language. (We hope that this marks the beginning of many such initiatives.). Also, thanks to Beshir Nakishbandi and Ottawa-Carleton Immigrant Services Organization (OCISO) for facilitating our Somali and Arabic family nights which helped us to initiate this project by contacting other Multicultural Liason Officers (MLOs) who helped with translations. Thanks go out to Kelly Wells, her staff at Chapters, Gloucester Center and to Jennifer Harman, Marketing Manager-Eastern Canada for Indigo Books and Music Inc.

We would like to thank all members of the Hawthorne School Council, who supported the initial concept and dedicated hours of their time. We particularly thank Council Co-President, Sharron Mahon, who shared her touching story 'My Grandmothers Quilt' at our kick-off assembly, donated time and treats at Translation Days, and offered help whenever we needed it. We thank Council Co-president, Sandy Cloutier-Wehbe, a tireless parent volunteer at the school, for her fund-raising efforts made on our behalf. Thanks go to Tamkeen Pirzada for all of her help with translation and to Reine Beale for her continued support.

Thanks to all of the teaching staff for inspiring their students to write excellent stories and for encouraging parents and families to translate. We appreciate their patience and support for Hawthorne Writes and the demands that it has placed on their time and energy. Special thanks to Amy Schaefer for undertaking the huge task of organizing the electronic copies, scanning and cropping translations, and working with students to build both our website and our book; Karen Selly for organizing stories and translations; Stephanie Ettinger for spearheading our in-school fund-raising efforts as well as assisting with the compilation of our book; Teresa Plumb for conducting the school census with her class as well as helping to ensure we met our deadlines; Marilyn Amey for organizing the donations and book orders; Wayne Simpson for promoting this project through the Hawthorne Herald and beyond; Richard Smith and Metrophotography for publicity.

Thanks to AnnieChuen Lau, Librarian; Scott Thompson, Computer technician; Sandy Labonte, Stefan Nichols and Claudette Dandy for preparing the library for our in-school translation workshop; Karen Skelly, Elaine Maynard, Carol Benson and Eleanor Mullins for photocopying and organizing stories; Amy Cole, Tracey Snow and Laura Cinkant who helped with fundraising; Jillian Soame for media contacts and story selections and Mary and Jim Dunne for helping to make sure our story selections represented our diverse community.

To all of the parents and family members who translated their children's stories with them, thank you for being our partners in education and for supporting us with your donations of time and money. We have done our best to identify as many translators as possible, however, several stories could not be matched with a translator. Our apologies if we have accidentally omitted your name, but please know that without your efforts, this book could not have been possible.

We would like to thank the student translators for doing an amazing job: Jaan Altosaar, Colin Wu, Djordje Djuric, Albert Alfaro, Sagal Dhurie, Lilia Lockwood, Sarah Beale, Jenny Liang, Shadman Zaman, Dararancy San, Sol Bee Kim, Somran Roy, Veli Selmani, Qianyu Zhang, and Xin Li.

We'd also like to thank the following people: Staff and Students of OCDSB International Language Programs, Anisa Metwally, Stefan Nichols, Isabel Doppelreiter, Tamkeen Pirzada, Kim Kangok, Viacheslav Bakhanovich, Susan Hafizi, Patricia Ables, Muntaser Hasan, Mr. Parekh, Anil Parekh, Kate Onukagha, Zhigang Liu, Bushra Gulzar, Douglas McKearken, Efrs Awil, Elena Creanga, Feryal El Khatin, Ghaji Siage, Glenn Brigaldino, Gunilla Axwik, Habte Araia, Humphrey Lin Tao Wang, Ibrahim Noor, Kimani Ng'ang'a, Ivy Tong, Abdi Aden, James Wang, Jayasri Kannan, Birhanu Tekle-Michael, Khadijeh Akbari, Khalida Hafizi, Bikhal Ismael, Krishnan Tirunellai, Lula Hared, Manoshi Kumar, Maria Jose Roldan Christina, Marisol E. Kwai, Ming Wang, Mohomad Barkhad, Mrs. Arulanantham, Aruna Gupta, Muneera Ali Al-Maghrebi, Nusrat Ali, Ola Al Azak, Oluyennsi Okorosobo, Annie Wong, Patricia Saunders, Abdulkadin Hussein, Rodaina Chalvour, S.S.Zahra Rizvi, Sahab Hussein Ismail, Saido Mohamed, Sairah Shahid, Sarah Elenezi, Shafiq Zaman, Abdelgadir Abbas, Sophie Kwok, Ahmed Omar, Sumaira Javedi, Suncica Bracika, Anneke Jansen Van Doorn Campbell, Abeer El-Khatib, Wen Rian, Xiaotong Yu, Xin Wang, and Yukie Fuchigami

Finally, thanks to Kelly Stanutz-Sedlar, Mireille Comte, Tracey Heard, Diana Molepo, and Aida Orfali and Richard Smith for last minute translations as we tried to get as many stories into the class versions as possible.

Thanks to all of the students involved with putting our stories online: Sarah Beale, Jens Brigaldino, Rutger Campbell, Nathan Chan, Adam Graham, Anish Krishnan, Lilia Lockwood, Olivia Maroun, Jessica Ostroff, Patrick Payne, Prashanth Srinivasan, Mara Van Baal, Meshach David, David Endemann, Jieyi Liang, Clayton Nguyen, Michael She, Charles Shen, Djordje Djuric, Hannah Saunders, Shadman Zaman, Stanley Tom, Somran Roy, Enochdaniel Okorosobo, Jaan Altosaar, James Cober, and Jennifer Sun. A special thanks to Dayla Goldberger, our ETI who was critical in running our two day Website Workshop at school in our computer lab. Also thank you to Christina Dumoulin, Kayla Talbot, Keleasha Marshall for helping us put our stories online, as well as Lisa Sleiman, Randy Granados-Portelance, James Cober, and Lucas Solenthaler for helping to research language statistics using www.ethnologue.com.

Thanks to all of the staff, parents, and volunteers who graciously read stories to help select a wide diversity of stories, languages, and experiences to include in this book.

And most importantly, thank you to all of the students and staff members for trusting their personal stories with us and for allowing us to share your stories with the world.

Due to the sheer magnitude of the project, we have inevitably left out names and organizations who have played a part in bringing Hawthorne Writes to light. For this, please accept our heartfelt apologies, and our thanks for your help in bringing our students stories to life.

Foreword

Reading. My favourite pastime. I like to read everything. Books, short stories, poems, newspapers. I read in quiet places like my living room and in busy places like an airport. Reading can take me to places that never were and to places that never will be. Reading can take me to places I have not yet visited or remind me of places I have been. Reading makes my mind work. Reading gives me things to think about that I would never otherwise imagine.

And who writes what I read? Sometimes I do -- in my journal or in magazines or books where I was lucky enough to be published. Sometimes the writers are famous people who make lots of money writing, or journalists who write about what they see or study. Sometimes the writers are students.

Writing is the other side of reading. You get to decide what to write about, what to include and what to leave out. Writing is much slower than talking so you can think carefully about what to write. And you can change it before anyone else reads it, which can be an advantage over talking.

Writing is important because it lets you express how you feel, it lets you share your thoughts with others, and it sometimes lets you persuade other people about something you feel strongly about. Your writing can be shared with many others over a long period of time. Writing makes you think about what you will put down on paper, and it teaches you the right way to say things. Because if you don't, people will not understand you.

Congratulations to all of the authors of this book! When I read your stories, I am able to share a little bit of your imagination and I feel I know you better. So keep reading! And keep writing!

Dr. Lorne Rachlis

Director of Education
Ottawa-Carleton District School Board

Dear Reader,

This book represents a snapshot of some of the different stories, cultures and languages present at Hawthorne. To spearhead Hawthorne Writes, from beginning to end, has been both an honour and an enormous risk. To have nearly 500 stories entrusted to you is a rare privilege and responsibility.

Stories are a part of us – recollections of both our personal lives and our family's history. In some cultures, stories represent a significant aspect of a person's life. Indeed, many students shared important anecdotes about family heirlooms, loved ones, or escapes from troubled lands. To have these stories translated into a first language is to ask our students to share their cultural and their linguistic roots.

Hawthorne Writes is a wonderful way to validate our students' culture and personal experiences as well as to empower them as authors. A book of this nature would be an impressive endeavour for any organization, let alone a public school. A lot of good can come from a book like this: The potential to break down barriers by finding similarities in experiences and languages is enormous.

Our project was defined by the school year which ends in June. For each child to receive a copy of the published book, strict deadlines had to be met. Due to these compressed timelines, my greatest fear was that we had inadvertently made a mistake along the way: incorrectly labelled a language or accidentally included a translated story upside down. As the stories and translations came in, I felt honoured that our students trusted us to keep their stories safe. I was also concerned that we would accidentally betray this trust through some mistake and alienate our students or families.

Omission, accidental or otherwise, can be hurtful. Whose stories have we given a voice to? Whose stories have we missed? What stereotypes have we accidentally portrayed or encouraged? Not all immigrants are visible minorities. Not all visible minorities are recent immigrants. Do our stories reflect this? What started as a well-intentioned project might have significant consequences to the reader.

I must apologize if we have not treated all stories equitably. Many stories were translated at home by friends and family members. Some of our students were unable to have their stories translated at home and so the onus was on us to translate the story. Although we made great efforts to translate them into the appropriate first language, this was not always possible due to time constraints, or the lack of translators.

Unfortunately these may have been the stories where translation was most meaningful as literacy support in the students' first language was not available at home. Although we have several students whose family roots lie in Jamaica, we were unable to capture their stories into Jamaican Creole (Patois). Their stories were translated into Korean, Albanian, or any other available languages, if at all. What a missed opportunity to empower these students by recognizing the language they hear when visiting relatives in Jamaica.

Although this book marks the culmination of a huge project for us, it also marks the beginning for others. There is a theory that a butterfly flapping its wings in one part of the world can cause a chain reaction that result in a tornado touching down in another part of the world. The "Butterfly Effect" predicts that small actions can have gigantic consequences. To this end, we hope that the passion demonstrated in Hawthorne Writes will spark others to initiate similar projects. Although the risk is great, the benefits of succeeding are equally great.

Mike Fuchigami
(Editor in Chief)

Introduction

This book is a celebration of literacy and of what it is to be a multicultural, multilingual community. Everyone has a story to share. Whether we are a new immigrant or a fifth generation Canadian, we have a story to share. In this book, we hope to celebrate the differences and the common elements that make us a vibrant, school community.

Hawthorne Writes is a multilingual book. Every student and staff member wrote a story in English and through partnership with parents, community members and the International Languages Program at Ottawa Carleton District School Board, these stories were translated into a heritage language. Many stories were translated at home; however this was not always possible. Some families have spoken English for generations; other families have lost their first language. Every effort was made to translate children's stories into their first language. We drew upon our community and the International Languages program to translate the remaining stories.

The selection committee was composed of parents, teachers, and volunteers who read and evaluated stories. Emphasis was placed on having a balance of stories representing the diversity of Hawthorne Public School classrooms (Regular program, ESL, SELC, GLP, and Gifted) and grade levels (Kindergarten to Grade 8). Emphasis was also placed on capturing a multicultural mix ranging from Canadian-born students whose first language is English, Canadian-born students whose mother tongue is not English and students who have recently immigrated to Canada.

We have selected and published stories that are culturally and linguistically representative of our students. Our goal is to celebrate the diversity we find in our school and in Canada by recognizing the value of multilingual literacy. We are offering this book to the global community by publishing in print and an on-line. Grandparents in Kuwait or Iqualuit will be able to read their grandchild's story in their mother tongue.

Students have been excited about this book from its introduction. Now, the book is a reality and every child at Hawthorne is a published author. Seventy stories have been selected for this publicly-available version. In addition, each child received their classmates' stories in a special classroom edition. Every child received a book with their story in it.

We hope you enjoy reading this book as much as we enjoyed writing it.

Mike Fuchigami
Susan Newton
Francesse Kopczewski

Hawthorne *Writes*
because everyone has a story...

YOUR FUTURE IS NOW

Class Stories – Mr. Braden (Grade 5/6)

My Family Treasure

My family treasure is a special carpet. The carpet is special to me because my grandmother gave it to me to celebrate my birth.

I've never met my grandmother because she lives so far away in Iran which used to be called Persia.

Persia is well known for making finely crafted carpets. My grandmother chose my carpet very carefully. She left her home in Tehran and visited the carpet stalls in Mashad. Carpets are handcrafted in Iran. Some are now made by weavers, but they still practice the art of hand knotting. Some carpets take years to hand knot. One family member may start a carpet and not finish it. The work is then finished by the next generation.

My special carpet is not very big. It's only 3 feet by 5 feet. My carpet is very fine because it has 725 knots per square inch. The more knots in a carpet the finer it is. The carpet hangs on our living room wall. This is because it is to fine to walk on.

The pattern on the carpet is called the garden and is signed by the person who made it . The carpet colour is brown, but changes colour with the light and angle of it. The pattern has many details of flowers, and leaves done in a box pattern woven with aqua, burgundy, and rusty hues.

The carpet is special to me because my grandmother gave it to me to celebrate my birth.

Arrian Amir-Rafiei, Grade 6 Student

मेरे परिवार में एक बहुत सी अच्छी एक पिछाना है। यह
पिछाना मुझे मेरी दादीमाने मेरी वर्षगांठ जिमेंते दिया था।
    मेरी दादीमा इशान देशमे, जो पहले परशिया के नाम से
जानने वाला, रहती है। में मेरी दादीमाको मिला नहीं हूं।
    परशिया अच्छे से अच्छी पिछाना बनाने मे बहुत
प्रसिद्ध है। मेरी दादीमाने मेरे लिये अच्छी पिछाना पंसद कीया।
मेरी दादीमा नरेशन से मासद खरिद्मी करने गइ थी। यह सब
पिछाने राथसे बांधके बनाये जाते है। कभी कभी, परिवार का
एक आदमी पिछाना बनाना शुरु करता है, वह काम इतना
दूसरा जनरेशन पूरा करता है।
    मेरी बहुत सी अच्छी पिछानी होती है। पिछाना 3 फीट
से ५ फीट का है। वह इतनी अच्छी ओर बही प्रत्येक है।
मेरा पिछाना ७२५ धाध से बनाया है - वो भी अलग बुक्स बे है।
जितने ज्यादा धाध उतने इतनी अच्छी पिछानी होती है।
मेरा यह पिछान मेरे घरकी दिवाल पे रखा है। दिवार के
उपर इशालिये के जिससे हम इसे इतनी तरह रख शके।
    मेरे पिछाने पर एक बगिये की तीखावने है। बनाने वालेने
ने उपर साईन किया है। वह ब्राइट रंग की है। जभी भी
उस पर लाइट होती है तब रंग बदलता है। पिछाने के उपर
फुल की रंग बेरंगी, बोश की तरह रंग है।
    यह पिछाना मुझे बहुत पंसद है क्योंकी मेरी दादीमा ने
अपनी शालगिराह पर दिया था।

Language: Hindi
Translated by: Anil Parekh

Joan

I'm going to write the story of my grandmother, Joan O'Connell. More specifically, the funny experiences my family has whenever she is near.

Joan O'Connell was born in Montreal, Quebec in 1930. Her parents were originally from Washington (or "Warshington" as she always says it) D.C. She was a very bright child who graduated early from high school and then went on to McGill University where she met a man who would later become her husband. They had three children, one of whom is my father. Later, she moved to Ottawa where she got her masters degree in history at Carleton University and eventually become the Prime Minister's director of correspondence.

That isn't the *real* Joan though. What I really want to tell you all about is how over the years, my grandmother has done some pretty funny things! My grandmother, for example, always called her sons by the wrong names. They had a dog named Smokey, and when she needed to call, for example, Jamie, she would sometimes yell: "Smokey...Ian...Brian...Jamie?"

In fact, this occurred so frequently that the boys invented a pretend Game Show that they called Famous Names. They imagined that the host would put their mother in a soundproof room and tell her the name of a famous person. When she was released from the room, she would have to tell a contestant the name as best as she could. The object of the game would be for the contestant to figure out what the name had been before it had been mangled.

One might think that she would do this because she is hard of hearing. Whether or not this is the reason that the boys thought of "Famous Names" one thing is certain: some of the *most* humorous experiences have to do with the fact that my grandmother's hearing is fading. I remember once when the

Sydney Fraser, Grade 5 Student

Trip 2004

In the summer of 2004 my family and I went to Macau, Hong Kong, and New Zealand to visit my aunts and uncles. Macau is one-hour ferry ride from Hong Kong in southern China.

Upon our arrival in Macau, I almost passed out because of the heat and humidity. It was hot! When we got to my grandpa's apartment, I realized that I would be sleeping on the 34th floor (I'm afraid of extreme heights). In Macau, we visited my mom's family, tasted some exotic Chinese food, and did some sightseeing around town. We stayed there for about 2 weeks, and then we went to New Zealand.

The month of July is the middle of winter in the southern hemisphere which is where New Zealand is. When we arrived at the Auckland airport, it was around 10°C. We stayed at my uncle's house. In New Zealand, houses rarely have heating, so we wore coats when we were awake and had electrically heated blankets when we slept. My uncle took us to a dead volcano. After a short stay in Auckland, we went on a nine-day bus tour in the south island of New Zealand. On the bus tour we saw the place where the movie "The Lord of the Rings" was filmed, the beach where Blue Footed penguins nested, and a Kiwi bird, the most endangered bird on the planet.

When we got back to Auckland, my uncle brought us to Rota Rua which is about 200 km north of Auckland. There we saw geysers, ate a Maori dinner, and saw Maori dancers. The Maoris were the native people of New Zealand. They look a lot like our natives in Canada.

We stayed in New Zealand for eleven days then we went to Hong Kong to see my cousin for 2 days. In Hong Kong, we didn't do much except for shopping and resting before a long flight back to Canada.

I really enjoyed my trip to Macau, Hong Kong and New Zealand because I saw my relatives that I had never met before. I am especially happy that I saw my grandma because she passed away almost a year after I saw her.

Richard Hum, Grade 5 Student

二零零四年的旅遊　譚建澄作

二零零四年的夏天我和我的家人去澳門、香港和新西蘭探我的姨媽和舅父。澳門是在南中國離香港一小時船程。

一到澳門我差不多暈倒空氣很熱和很潮濕,真熱!到公公的住所才知道我要睡在大廈的三十四樓,我很怕極高的。我們大均在澳門住了兩個星期,探了媽媽的親人,吃了新奇的中國食品和四處遊覽,然後去新西蘭。

新西蘭在南半球七月是那裏的冬季中期,當我們抵達奧克蘭的機場時氣溫大均是攝氏十度,我們住在二舅父的家。在新西蘭的屋大都沒有暖氣,日間要穿樓,晚間睡覺時要蓋電毯,舅父帶我們去遊死火山,我們在奧克蘭小住便去南島參加一個九天的巴士團。遊了名片的拍片場地,去過藍色腳企鵝住的沙灘,見過世界面臨絕種最危險的獅猴桃鳥。

返回奧克蘭舅父帶我們去離奧克蘭北面二百公里的一個地方,在那裏我們見過間歇噴泉,吃了毛利晚餐,觀看毛利舞蹈表演。毛

利人是新西蘭的原著人、樣子很像加拿大的原著人。

我們在新西蘭住了十一天後去香港探表親。在香港我們祇留

了兩天、購物和休息準備回加拿大、一個很長的飛行旅程。

我有一個很愉快的澳門、香港和新西蘭旅行，見到我從未見

過的親戚，我特別開心見過婆婆，她在我探過她一年多後便離

開了世界。

Language: Chinese
Translated by: Sophie Kwok

My Warhammer Army

I collect these toy soldiers from a game called Warhammer 40,000. It is a strategic battle board game with miniatures that you glue and paint yourself; so you can customize it. There are a lot of races [meaning species of army with there own background and units] such as the good old orks and chaos.

My army is the Space marines of the mighty Imperial domain. I started collecting Warhammer a couple of years ago when I went into a Warhammer store and saw such awesome figures I had to do some of my own so I was hooked.

The name I gave my warriors was "Legion Artimes". I think this is a good name because the Greek goddess of the hunt was named Artimes and also I was reading "Artimes Fowl" the third book. After that I thought a forest look was in order. So I put in some dark greens and browns and came up with a masterpiece but my brother thought that we should paint the muzzle of the helmet red to give a feral look and like he just ate a bloody meal. After that we made a masterpiece better, ever since the Legion Artimes has spread the Emperors justice to many enemies.

My Dad and my brother Daniel collect Warhammer too. My Dad owns a war band of orks, a bunch of choppers in close quarters fighting. My brother Daniel owns something the complete opposite of Dad, called the Tau who specializes in long range bombardment

My experiences in Warhammer have been a blast. I have played one or two outside games but I have played many games with my brother and my Dad in which I usually win or get into a draw but the point is I am good at it. I think everyone should play Warhammer 40k because it is a great game.

Anthony Kolish, Grade 6 Student

Моя Warhammer Армия.

Я колекциомирую этих игрушечных солдатиков из игры под названием Warhammer 40.000. Это настольная игра о стратегии сражения с маленькими фигурками, которые вы можете склеивать и раскрашивать, так что вы можете управлять ей. Она состоит из большого количества различных армейских подразделений со своими собственными отрядами и обмундированием.

Моя Армия - это Космические морские пехотинцы могущественной Империи. Я начал собирать Warhammer пару лет назад когда я зашёл в Warhammer магазин и увидел эти замечательные фигурки которые я должен был собирать и совершенствовать самостоятельно, так что я сразу же увлёкся ими.

Я назвал своих воинов „Artimes легион" Я думаю, это хорошее имя потому что греческого бога охоты звали Artimes и я тогда читал третью книгу под названием Artimes-птицелов. После этого лес выглядел естественно. Я добавил немного темнозеленого и коричнево и сделал отличный экземпляр, но мой брат решил, что лучше покрасить шлем в красный свет, как будто этот дикарь только что съел свою кровавую добычу. После этого мы улучшили свой экземпляр, после этого Империя покорила много своих врагов.

Мой папа и брат Данила тоже собира

У моего брата Данилы, наоборот, есть группа Тау, которая специализируется в дальнем обстреле.

У меня огромной опыт в этой игре. Иногда я играл на улице, но я предпочитаю играть в Warhammers с моим отцом и Данилой, потому что я всегда побеждаю.

Я думаю, все должны играть в эту чудесную игру Warhammers 40.000

Language: Russian
Translated by: Viacheslav Bakhanovich

YOUR FUTURE IS NOW

A Family Memory

I remember when I was just about 6, and almost every day my grandpa would take me hiking up a mountain for exercise. We would always bring snacks and drinks and sometimes a tent. When we got up the lush green mountain we would go to our favourite spot at the top of the mountain, which was a flat stable rock that provided a great view of the side of the mountain. Usually when we get there we would eat the snacks and explore more of the mountain. If we bring the tent then we would camp out for a few hours, and if one of us gets bored then we'd go out and play with echoes on the mountain next to us. It was the most fun I think I would ever have in my life. After we got back from the mountain my mom and grandma would greet us with a delicious lunch of rice and vegetables. The love from my grandpa is always in my mind.

Guozhen La, Grade 5 Student

我的家庭記憶

當我六歲的時候，我的祖父會和我一起去爬山。我們會帶吃的和喝的，有時候也會帶一個帳篷。當我們爬到山頂上，我們就會去我們最喜歡的地方。我們最喜歡的地方是一個又大又平的岩石在山頂上。我們到達的時候會一邊吃東西一邊去探測這個山。如果我們把我們的帳篷帶來了，我們就會在山上紮營下。我們也會用我們的山旁邊的山玩一個〈回音〉的遊戲。

這是我最喜歡的家庭活動。這真是一個很好玩的經驗。當我們從山上回來的時候，我的媽媽和我的伯母會做一個很好吃的午餐。我會永遠地記得我的祖父的愛。

Language: Chinese
Translated by: Jenny Liang

My Trip To China

In the summer of 2005, my mother and I went to China for three weeks. We had to go on a plane to go to China we spent sixteen hours on a plane! The plane food was disgusting to me, well some of it was good.

When we first arrived at Beijing, I had to adjust to the air there because the air was really thick and smoggy, I also had to adjust to the time change there. The air there wasn't like Canada's air, the air there was hard to breath in like when you put a plastic bag over your mouth. It was very hot in China, the temperature was around 35 to 45 degrees each day. Also, I noticed that you can barely see the sun, all that you can see is the outline of the sun because in China it's as if there's fog twenty four seven!

My distant relative came with his friend to pick us up. When we were driving around, I noticed when I was in China was that everyone lived in an apartment (almost everyone). My mother and I stayed in Beijing for a week, and throughout the week, we went to different places like the Great Wall, Qin Ming tombs, and the Forbidden Palace. At the Great Wall, it was very humid and hot but despite that, my mother and I still climbed it. We only had an hour so we didn't go everywhere on the Great Wall (if we did, I would have been really sore the next day). When we went to the Qin Ming tombs, It was also very warm and sunny. There were artefacts there and personally, they didn't look that important to me. What's an old deformed hat worth? At the Forbidden palace, it was fun because it had a great view of Beijing and these photographers took pictures of us in old fashioned Chinese clothing. At every place we visited, I bought a souvenir. You know why? Because I feel that when you buy a souvenir, it reminds you of the place you bought that souvenir from and so those memories will last forever.

After a week of staying in Beijing, my aunt came to pick up my mother and to go to Tianjing. While we were there, we went to lots of restaurants, malls, and flea markets. At the restaurants, obviously the food there was Chinese food but to me, that was bad because I'm allergic to a very important ingredient in Chinese food: msg. The malls were huge! I could shop all day there. At some stores and flea markets, unlike Canada, you can negotiate for the pricing, in a way that's good because you can get the item for a low price, but in a way it's bad because some shop owners will try to rip you off.

We stayed there two weeks and then we went back to Canada. The whole ride took seventeen hours! Imagine that, seventeen long hours on an airplane and it was really boring. Other than that, the plane food was still disgusting but, the view of the islands off the coast of British Columbia were magnificent!

Rosey Li, Grade 6 Student

Meine Reise nach China

Im Sommer 2005 war ich mit meiner Mutter für drei Wochen in China. Der Flug hat sechzehn Stunden gedauert! Das Essen am Flieger war auch nicht wirklich das Beste.

Nach unsrer Ankunft in Beijing musste ich mich zuerst einmal an die Luftfeuchtigkeit, den Smog und an die Zeitumstellung gewöhnen. Die Luft war nicht mit der in Kanada zu vergleichen. Das Atmen war schwer, es hat sich angefühlt, als hätte man Plastik vor dem Mund. Es war extrem heiß in China, wir hatten Temperaturen um die 45 Grad jeden Tag. Mir fiel auch auf, dass es fast unmöglich war die Sonne zu sehen, man konnte nur Umrisse erkennen, denn es gibt keinen Tag ohne den Smog.

Ein Verwandter kam mit einem Freund, um uns anzuholen. Was mir sofort aufgefallen ist, ist, dass niemand dort ein eigenes Haus zu haben scheint, es wimmelt jedoch von Wohnblöcken. Meine Mutter und ich blieben in Beijing für eine Woche und während dieser Zeit haben wir viele Sehenswürdigkeiten besucht wie z.B: die Chinesische Mauer, Qin Ming´s Grabstätte und den Verbotenen Palast. Trotz der feuchten Hitze sind meine Mutter und ich auf die Chinesische Mauer geklettert, wir hatten nur eine Stunde Zeit, also konnten wir nicht wirklich viel darauf herum spazieren. (Hätten wir den Tag dort oben verbracht hätten wir sicher einen ziemlichen Muskelkater). Die Hitze war auch ein Teil unsres Besuches der Qin Ming Grabstätte. Es gab dort viele Artefakte zu bestaunen, aber ich muss zugeben, dass ich persönlich nicht wirklich davon beeindruckt war. Wie kann ein alter verformter Hut denn etwas wert sein? Den meisten Spaß hatte ich, als wir den Verbotenen Palast besucht haben. Man hatte eine wunderbare Aussicht auf Beijing und ein Fotograph hat Bilder von uns in alter chinesischer Tracht gemacht. Ich habe ein Souvenir von jeder Sehenswürdigkeit gekauft. Wisst Ihr warum? Wenn du dir ein Souvenir kaufst, dann wird es dich immer an diesen Platz erinnern und du kannst es nie vergessen.

Nachdem wir eine Woche in Beijing waren, kam meine Tante , um mich und meine Mutter abzuholen, um nach Tianjing zu fahren. Während unsres Aufenthaltes dort, aßen wir in vielen Lokalen, waren in Einkaufszentren und Flohmärkten.

Natürlich gab es in den Lokalen hauptsächlich Chinesisches Essen und meine Allergie zu einer der wichtigsten Zutaten (msg) macht es nicht gerade leicht. Die Einkaufszentren waren riesig, ich könnte einen ganzen Tag dort verbringen. In manchen Geschäften und auf den Flohmärkten kann man über den Preis verhandeln. Dies ist einerseits gut, da man recht gute Dinge zu niedrigen Preisen erhandeln kann, aber manchmal steigt auch der Geschäftsinhaber besser aus.

Wir blieben noch zwei Wochen bevor wir zurück nach Kanada kamen. Der Rückflug hat siebzehn Stunden gedauert. Stellt Euch siebzehn Stunden auf einem Flieger vor. Ziemlich langweilig. Das Essen war genauso ungenießbar wie auf dem Hinflug, aber die Aussicht auf die Küste von British Columbia war wundervoll.

Language: German
Translated by: ???

Sweet Tea and Bitter Tea

"Ten Ren". Does this name sound familiar to you? If it doesn't, let me tell you that it is an excellent, worldwide tea company which sells a variety of products such as teapots, bubble tea, tea snacks, and most important of all, tea. If you haven't seen or been to a Ten Ren store you might want to look out for it because you're going to discover who founded this splendid company, troubles he had to face, and strategies he used to make a common store into one of the best selling tea companies in Taiwan.

My great-uncle, Re-ho Lee was born in 1935 in a poor tea farming family in southern Taiwan. His family owned several tea fields and was connected immensely to tea. Re-ho was doing extremely hard tasks at the age of 12 and being the eldest of the 8 children, was given great responsibilities. But since tea farming was very common back then, you don't get a lot of money being a tea farmer. At the age of 16, Re-ho's family was forced to sell the tea fields and move up to central Taiwan where he and his dad opened a tea shop and started life as a tea merchant to make a living.

Life as a tea merchant isn't that easy either. Re-ho had to bike about 100 kilometres a day to deliver and sell the tea leaves. But Re-ho had several strategies up his sleeve. Before selling the tea leaves, he made friends with clients and find out what they liked. Also, he kept track of when the clients bought the tea and when they are likely to run out, therefore, he didn't need to go when not necessary. Also, if the clients weren't home, he placed the tea in the house all the same, so he didn't have to go extra miles. With his amiable manner and intelligent strategies, he made steady business and a lot of friends. He biked for 4 years, from when he was 16, to when he was 20, and finally, in 1959, he bought a humble motorcycle that saved him the bother of biking and in 1961, he married a village counselor's daughter and had three children.

Then, he moved to Taipei (the capital of Taiwan) which had a far greater population than central Taiwan so that he could make more money and better business. At first, he wasn't really known in Taipei, but he also has a few more strategies. He build his shop next to a popular tea shop so that after shopping at the popular tea shop, people would go and check out the new tea shop which Re-ho called "Ten Ren". There, he would put the other merchandise from the other store in a bigger "Ten Ren" bag therefore advertising the new tea shop. That time, none of the store clerks in Taiwan wore uniforms, but Re-ho gave his store clerks uniforms to show how organized of the company is. Most company advertises in newspapers, but Re-ho thought it wasn't enough. To advertise, he went around the country on a wagon, giving out samples as to attract public attention. He also placed a fan at the back of the store to spread the aroma of his tea leaves. But he wasn't done there. He knew that Japanese tea is much further developed than Taiwanese ones, so he visited Japan, visiting the tea farms and trying out the specimens and high-tech tea making machines. He saw theirs and started using high-tech devices to make his tea. Also, he decorated his shops with attractive plastic leaves on strings hanging from the ceiling that sways gently in the wind, creating a bliss atmosphere.

His tea shop soon became Taipei's most famous tea company. The fame and quality of Ten Ren's quickly spread, making his tea company rich and famous. In August of 1988, he opened a stock exchange, not knowing that it will cause trouble.

Two years later in 1990, the manager of the stock exchange committed an economical crime, fining Re-ho 3 billion NT (New Taiwanese Dollar), bankrupting the company. He feels that Ten Ren is no longer safe under his control, so he let his eldest son take his place and started a new tea company in China. He and his wife went around China, visiting the other tea companies to see what the Chinese are used to. Finally, after several years, he formed his new tea company "Ten-Fu". Ten-Fu's fame quickly spread, making him as rich and famous as he was in Taiwan. The fame was so great that the APEC used Ten-Fu's tea as a souvenir to tourists. Because of that, the company was known worldwide. But Re-ho still had some ideas for his company. Since bathrooms have a reputation of being "unclean", he made his bathroom spotless and to show it, he invited some of his friends to a feast in the bathroom! Re-ho then saved up and in 2002, he opened his own tea museum, attracting countless tourists. Recently, he invented a "tea restaurant" where every dish is added a tea flavor. This restaurant is widely popular in Taiwan, China and Los Angelos.

To him, all the troubles and failures he faced felt like a cup of bitter tea, and after the bitterness, he finally got to taste the sweetness of success.

Humphrey Lin, Grade 6 Student

香茶和苦茶 Humphrey

你對天仁這個名字熟悉? 如果你不知道,就讓我告訴你,它是一家很好、全球知名的茶業公司,它販售許多產品,例如茶壺 、珍珠奶茶、茶點以及茶葉。如果你不曾看過或到過天仁茶行,你或許會想看看。因為你會發現是誰創辦這個很好的公司,他面對的困難,他如何將一個平凡的小店變成台灣最大的茶業公司,他的策略是什麼?

我的叔公李瑞河,1935 出生在貧窮的南臺灣茶農家庭。他家有一些茶園,瑞河在 12 歲時就極為辛苦的工作,他是家中 8 個孩子中的老大, 責任重大。種茶在那時十分平常,賺不了多少錢 。在 16 歲時,瑞河的家庭被迫賣茶園,並搬到中台灣。他和他的爸爸以開茶業店為生。

茶商的生活也不容易。瑞河必須每天騎腳踏車到大約 100 公里外的地方運送和賣茶葉。但瑞河有幾個戰略,在賣茶葉之前,他與客戶交朋友並發現他們喜歡什麼,並且他記錄下客戶買了什麼茶並且他們可能何時用盡,因此, 他不需要不必要的時候前往。如果客戶不在家時, 他會把茶葉留下, 因此他沒有必須再度前往。他以和藹可親的方式以及聰明的策略,他平穩的經營並交了很多好朋友。他騎了 4 年腳踏車, 從當他是 16 歲到 20 歲, 終於在 1959 年他買了了一輛不好的摩托車, 1961 年他與村長的女兒結婚並有三個孩子。

然後他搬到有更多的人口的臺北(臺灣的首都) 以便他能賺更多的錢和更好的生意。起初, 他不真正了解臺北,但是他有更多策略。他在一家知名的茶葉店邊開了他的茶葉商店,瑞河把這家店取名為天仁。他會把顧客由另一商店購買的商品裝在一個更大的天仁袋子內,此舉可為這家新茶商店做廣告。那時在台灣沒有售貨員穿制服,但是瑞河給他的售貨員制服,以顯示這家公司是有組織的。大多數公司多在報紙做廣告, 但瑞河認為不夠。為了做廣告,他開貨車四處走動, 分送樣品吸引人們的注意。他並且在商店的後面安置一臺風扇以散播他店中的茶葉芳香。他知道,日本茶藝比臺灣茶更先進,因此他訪問日本, 參觀茶農場和試驗標本和高技術茶機器。並且, 他以吸引力的塑料葉子在串垂懸從柔和地搖擺在風的天花板裝飾了他的店,製造極樂氣氛。

他的茶商店很快成為臺北的最著名的茶公司,天仁的名望和品質迅速傳播開了, 他的茶公司更富有也出名了。在 1988 年 8 月, 他打了證券交易所,他還不知道, 它將導致麻煩。

二年後, 在 1990 年, 證券交易所的經理犯了經濟罪, 天仁被罰款三十億新臺幣, 他公司破產了。他認為天仁在他手下不再是安, 因此他讓他的長子取代他的地位,他到中國建立了一個新茶公司。他和他的妻子在中國四處走動, 參觀其它茶公司,看什麼中國人的習慣。終於, 在幾年以後,他建立了他的新茶公司"天福" 。

天福的名聲迅速傳播開, 使他像他在臺灣一樣富有和著名。他很出名, APEC 用了天福的茶作為紀念品對旅客。由於此事,全世界都知道這家公司。但瑞河對他的公司仍然有一些想法。因為廁所一般來說是"髒的", 他為顯示他的廁所一塵不染,他邀請了一些他的朋友在廁所中餐宴! 瑞河存錢,在 2002 年他開了他自己的茶博物館, 吸引不計其數的遊人。最近, 他發明了一家"茶餐館", 每道菜中都有茶的味道。這家餐館在臺灣、中國和 Los Angelos 很普遍。

對他而言, 所有麻煩和失敗像一杯苦澀茶, 並且在苦澀以後, 他最後品嘗成功的甜美。

Language: Mandarin
Translated by: ???

New York City

_____

During March break, my family and I went to New York City and stayed in the Travel Inn hotel. While we were there we did many things like, going on the Staten Island Ferry and seeing the Statue of Liberty. It wasn't that much fun because people are not allowed inside the Statue of Liberty anymore. I was disappointed considering I was looking forward to going up it. Apparently it closed the day the Twin Towers were knocked down.

After that we went to the Natural History Museum and there was a room full of butterflies and plants. The butterflies would land on you if you put your arm out. Then we went to a different room that had the largest meteorite in the world! The rest of that floor was full of diamonds, crystal, silver and gold. After we watched a movie about the Galapagos Islands that has no humans, just animals and hardly any plants. Maybe a few biologists would go there every once in a while.

The next day we went to Central Park to watch the St. Patrick's Day parade and I video taped some of it. I have to say that most of it was Scottish. We walked around Central Park and saw the statue of Balto who was the main character in my favorite childhood book. If you want to know what it's about I'm sure your local library would be happy to lend it to you☺.

We also went on the observation deck of the Rockefeller Center to see the whole city, I looked through the binoculars and saw Central Park so clearly that it felt like I was in a two story building right next to it!

When we left to go shopping, my sister accidentally flagged down a limo! The driver said he would drive us to the store for 10 bucks. My mom thought it was a good idea and my sister I went into a limo for the first time.

We walked past MTV at the exact time Natalie Portman was in there, who ever she is? A girl told us who she was and that she was being interviewed for her most recent movie called V for Vendetta.

The next day we went to a flea market, which is basically a place full of tents and people selling things in them like jewelry, shoes, handbags and china. Then we got packed up for our long ride home.

OH, Yeah on the way to New York we saw a war ship with jets on top (it was 1/2 a KM. Long and 5 floors high!

Ciara Matthews, Grade 6 Student

La ciudad de Nueva York

Durante las vacaciones de marzo, mi familia y yo fuimos a la ciudad de Nueva York y nos hospedamos en el hotel Travel Inn. Hicimos muchas cosas en Nueva York, por ejemplo, viajamos en el Ferry Staten Island y visitamos la Estatua de la Libertad. El viaje no fue muy agradable porque no permitían a la gente dentro de la Estatua de la Libertad. Me desilucioné muchísimo porque estaba ansioso de subir a la Estatua de la Libertad. Al parecer la cerraron el día en que las Torres Gemelas se derrumbaron.

Luego fuimos al Museo de Historia Natural y allí había un cuarto lleno de mariposas y plantas. Las mariposas se posaban en nuestro brazo si lo extendíamos. Después fuimos a otro cuarto en el cual se encontraba el meteorito más grande del mundo! El resto del piso estaba lleno de diamantes, cristales, plata y oro. Tuvimos oportunidad de ver una película sobre la Isla Galápagos en la cual no viven seres humanos, sólo animales y algunas plantas. Sólo algunos biólogos visitan

Al día siguiente fuimos a "Central Park", a ver un desfile en el día de San Patricio donde tuve la oportunidad de grabar el desfile. La mayoría de los participantes eran escoceses. Caminamos por el "Central Park" y vimos la estatua de Balto quién era uno de los protagonistas más importantes en mi libro favorito durante mi infancia. Si tienes interés en saber más acerca de este libro, lo puedes obtener en la biblioteca.

Fuimos al piso de observación del "Rockefeller Centre" y observamos toda la ciudad. Use los anteojos de larga vista para ver "Central Park" y se veía tan claro que sentí que estaba en un edificio muy cerca del parque!

Cuando nos preparábamos a ir de compras, mi hermana detuvo a una limosida sin darse cuenta. El chofer exclamó que nos llevaría al negocio por diez dólares. Mi mama pensó que era una buena idea y mi hermana y yo nos subimos a la limosina por primera vez.

Caminamos hacia MTV al mismo tiempo en que Natalie Portman se encontraba allí, quienquiera que sea ella? Una niña nos dijo quien era Natalie Portman y que la estaban entrevistando por su película más reciente "V for Vendetta."

Al día siguiente fuimos al mercado de las pulgas, que practicamente es un lugar lleno de carpas y gente vendiendo joyas, zapatos, carteras y loza. Después empacamos nuestras cosas para regresar a casa.

Oh, yeah al regresar a Nueva York vimos un barco de guerra con aviones El barco medía aproximadamente medio kilómetro de largo y cinco pisos de alto.

Language: Spanish
Translated by: Marisol E. Kwai

A Kid's Life

India is a vast country located in the northern hemisphere. It is surrounded by the Indian Ocean in the south, Atlantic Ocean in the east and Arabian Sea in the west. The Bay of Bengal, which is located in India, has the largest shoreline of bays. The country has a variation of climates which range from cold, to boiling. Although India is a hot country, almost one tenth of it is covered in snow.

India is a very diverse country. It is a mix of different cultures and traditions. People from all over India immigrate to Canada because it offers great economic opportunities, better living standard and dazzling landscape. Many people emigrate from India every year to see Canada's diversity.

My name is Vivek and I grew up in an East Indian family. My name means "discretion". Although I was born in Canada, till the age of three, I only spoke in Gujarati, my native language. From nursery rhymes to the alphabet, I only spoke in my mother tongue.

Gujarati is a language spoken in the state of Gujarat in India.

My parents are first generation immigrants from India. My father came to Canada 20 years ago. He did a Masters in Mechanical Engineering. He emigrated because he wanted a better education and better life. My mother came to Canada when she was only a teenager. It took her 6 months to get habituated to the language and the culture. She has a Bachelor degree in Science. Although my parents could speak English fluently, they wanted to teach me my mother tongue.

When I was only 6-10 months old, my grand parents took care of me when my parents were busy. They were my favourite people who told me stories, read Gujarati books and played with me. My grand parents also did jigsaw puzzles with me.

At that time, my favourite food was idli sambhar. Idli sambhar are steamed rice cakes in a spicy curry with vegetables.

At the age three, I started going to school. For two weeks, I could not understand what my teachers were saying. Since I didn't know English, I spoke to my teacher in Gujarati. Instead of talking, I showed my teacher sign language. I learned English by listening to others and look at my teacher using sign language and interpreting the actions. After, I started picking up English. Within two months, I was good in English and enjoyed playing with others.

Subsequent to learning English, I started to enjoy TV shows. The first program that I watched was the 100 metre dash, in where Donovan Bailey set a world record for the fastest time during the 1996 Summer Olympics.

Along with learning English in school, I also learned French. I still read, write, comprehend and speak my mother tongue. I attend Gujarati school every week. I participate in the Gujarati cultural activities.

On a whole, my life as a child growing up is very exiting, ecstatic, exhilarating, comical, interesting, fun and, of course educational.

Vivek Parekh, Grade 6 Student

એક નાના છોકરાની જીંદગી

ભારત દેશ ઉત્તર ગોળાર્ધમાં આવેલો છે. દક્ષિણ દિશામાં હિંદ સમુદ્ર, આરબસાગરીક સમુદ્ર પૂર્વ દિશામાં અને અરબી સમુદ્ર પશ્ચિમ દિશામાં છે. બંગાળની ખાડી ભારતની લોબામાં લાંબો દરીયો કિનારો છે. આરતનો વિશાળ દેશનું હવામાન ઠંડીથી ધખધખ ગરમ છે. જોકે ભારત દેશ મોટે ભાગે ગરમ પ્રદેશ છે, પરંતુ ૬૦% હંમેશા બરફથી છવાયલું છે.

ભારત દેશ ધાગોર જુદી જુદી ભાતના ધીમીથી ભરપુર છે. આ ધાગોર બહુતની પ્રધાનો છે. ધણા લોકો ભારતમાં કેનેડા પોતાની આર્થિક પરિસ્થિતિને સુધારવા અને સારૂ જીવન ધોરણ મેળવવા આવે છે. ધણા લોકો ભારતમાં કેનેડા દર વર્ષે આવે છે.

મારૂ નામ વિવેક છે અને હું ભારતીય વારસાથી આવું છું. વિવેકનો અર્થ શાણપણ છે. જોકે, હું અહીં કેનેડામાં જન્મ્યો છું, ત્યાં સુધી ત્રણ વર્ષનો ત્યાં સુધી હું મારી આઝ્ગાભાષા ગુજરાતીમાં જ બોલી શક્તો. ઢકો બારમસિક ગીતો હું ગુજરાતીમાં શીખ્યો. ગુજરાતી ભાષા ભારતનો ગુજરાત રાજ્યમાં બોલાય છે.

મારા માબાપ ભારતથી આવી અહીં રહ્યા છે. મારા પિતા ૨૦ વર્ષ પહેલાં અહીં આવ્યા અને એમને એન્જીનિયર એરણબર્ડરીગમાં ભણ્યા. મેંગો અહીં સારૂ ભાગવત અને સારી જીંદગી ગાળવા અહીં આવ્યા. મારી આ મા અમારે હિઝમેગર હતાં ત્યારે આવ્યા. તેમને અંગ્રેજ ભાષા શીખતા છ મહીના લાગ્યા. એમને સાયરસમાં ઉચ્ચ ડીગ્રી મેળવી છે. જોકે, મારા માબાપ ધણુંજ સારૂ અંગ્રેજ બોલી શકે છે, પરંતુ તેમણે ગભે બાબબમાં ગુજરાતી ભાષા શીખવાની વૃત્તિ આપી.

હું જ્યારે કૂલ્ ૨૦ મહીનાનો હતો ત્યારે મારી દાદીમાં અને મારાના ત્યારે મારા માબાપ ડાક્તરા હતાં. મારી દાદીમાં મારી ધાર્મીક મિ... અને વારસા જતા. તે ગભે પરમ અને વાતો શીખવતી. એ સાથે હિંદી સંસ્કાર અને લ્યજર લાગ્યા.

ત્રણ વર્ષનો ઉંમરે, મેં શાળામાં ભણાવવું સારૂ કર્યું. પહેલા નર્સિકવારડીમાં મને અંગ્રેજ જ બોલવાને લાધે ધણી તકલીફ પડી. પરંતુ બીજા દોસ્તગમ્કો સાથે રહેતાં મને અંગ્રેજ આવડી ગયું. બે મહીનામાં તો હું અંગ્રેજ ધણુ સારૂ બોલતો અંગ્રેજ શીખ્યા પછી, મને દિલ્લીના પ્રોગ્રામમાં ભણવા મૂકવા આવ્યા. ૧૯૬૬ ઉનાળામાં ઓલોગપિશમ જોવું. કેનેડાનાં ઓઢાપણ જોઇલા ૧૦૦ કિસ્તની હોડમાં ભળ્યા.

આજે હું અંગ્રેજ સાથે, હિન્દ્ય પણ ભણ્યું છું. અને એવ્ ગુજરાતી ભણતો, વાંચતો અને બોલતા આવડે છે. હું ગુજરાતી પ્રોગ્રામમાં ભાગ લઉં છું. આજ, આને મારી જીંદગી ધાર્મીક ભારતની, ઔૂ વાળા અને રસાળ, અને શિસ્ત ભરેલી છે.

Language: Gujarati
Translated by: Mr. Parekh

YOUR FUTURE IS NOW

My Pet Dog

I would like to tell you what happened when I got my pet dog. It all started on a normal day when I was home. I was doing my homework when my dad came in. He talked to my mom for a while. I tried to eavesdrop but I couldn't understand what they were saying. About an hour later when I was watching television my dad came in. He reminded me of how I have always wanted a pet dog. Then he said the most beautiful words I have ever heard in my life: "I found a dog that needs a good owner and we're thinking about adopting it." I went crazy. I was so happy. I ran around the house yelling and laughing.

The next day we went to see the dog. Her name was Roxi and she was 9 months old at the time. She was black and had spots of brown. She was so cute. I played fetch with her for a while. Then when my dad asked me if I liked her I said, "Yes! Can we have her?" My dad chuckled a bit. "We'll go to get her tomorrow." said my dad.

The next day we went by to get her. When we brought her home she wasn't so sure about our house. She felt kind of sad. I stayed with her the whole night. She would bark whenever she heard a noise. Then she would come lick my face. It was very hard to get any sleep.

After a few days she got used to our house. She knew where her bed was and where her food, water, and toys were. I also taught her a few tricks. I taught her to fetch and sit and lay down. From then on I knew I would have to take good care of her.

Dogs are really great and loyal pets but they are also a big responsibility. So, if you're planning to get a dog, be prepared to change its water and fill its food bowl and have it wake you up at night and pick up after it. But in the end it is all worth it.

Now whenever I come home she greets me with a dancing body and a wagging tail and she jumps from couch to couch. And when I take her outside she always gets wet. She loves to chase the birds around the field. When she finds a stick she gives it to me so we can play fetch.

And when I pet her I feel her soft black fur and I can see she is happy in our home.

Sometimes we take her to Conroy pit. It's a big park where dogs can play. It's like a forest with some open areas. Whenever we go there Hunter comes with us. He is like a cheetah: very fast. Hunter is my dad's friend's dog. He is bigger then Roxi and he is the same breed as her. They are both German Shepherds. They chase after each other and when someone throws a stick they race to it. Hunter usually wins. When they see other dogs they run straight to them as if their hearts depended on it and start sniffing the other dogs. The problem is that when we go to the car Roxi pulls towards other dogs and the moving cars. And on the car ride home she walks around the back seat and sticks her head out the window. She is always so excited when we get home.

The meaning of this story is that if you are getting a pet be prepared to take care of it forever. Pets aren't for fun, they are for life. If you decide that today you want to buy a pet remember that you are going to have to take care of it, especially kittens and puppies. They will make your life a lot happier. And when you are sad they will always come to your side so you can pet them as though they were a great big fuzzy ball. But you must teach the fuzz ball some tricks like sit and down and fetch. It will stay with you for quite a long time. You must also pick up the dung. Also some places do not allow dogs like some parks. You must also look out for the dog. If you are planning to get a dog think what type of person you are. Like if you're a lazy person you would get a lazy dog or if you are active you would get an active dog.

Well, that is my memory about my dog, Roxi. Hope you've enjoyed it.

Radu Petre Pleacoff, Student

Cainele meu

As vrea sa va spun cum a fost cand l-am primit pe cainele meu. Totul a inceput intr-o zi ca oricare alta, cand eram acasa. Cand tatal meu a sosit acasa eu imi faceam temele. Tatal si mama mea vorbeau ceva intre ei, si desi am incercat sa trag cu urechea, nu am inteles ce spuneau. Cam peste o ora ma uitam la televizor, cand tatal meu a intrat. Mi-a adus aminte cat de mult imi doream eu un caine al meu. Apoi a spus cele mai frumoase cuvinte pe care le-am auzit in viata mea: "Am gasit un caine care are nevoie de un stapan bun si ne-am gandit sa-l adoptam noi". N-am mai putut de bucurie. Am inceput sa topai prin casa plin de veselie, strigand si razand in acelasi timp.

A doua zi am mers sa vedem cainele. Numele ei este Roxi si ea avea 9 luni. Avea blana neagra cu pete maro. Era asa frumoasa. M-am jucat cu ea, apoi tatal meu m-a intrebat daca imi place. "Da! Poate sa fie a mea?"am spus. Tatal meu a ras si a zis: "O s-o luam maine."

Ziua urmatoare am adus-o acasa, dar ea nu prea se simtea in largul ei. Era trista asa ca am stat langa ea toata noaptea. Latra la cel mai mic zgomot si apoi venea sa ma linga pe fata. Nu prea am dormit in acea noapte.

Dupa cateva zile s-a obisnuit in casa noastra. Stia deja care este locul ei, si unde erau mancarea, apa si jucariile ei. Din acel moment am stiut ca va trebui sa am grija de ea.

Cainii ne sunt prieteni loiali, dar si o mare responsabilitate. Deci, daca te gandesti sa ai un catel, va trebui sa-i schimbi si apa, si sa-i umpli castronul cu mancare. Uneori te va trezi noaptea, si trebuie sa aduni dupa el. Dar merita!

Acum, cand ma intorc acasa, ma intampina dand din coada si alergand in jurul meu si prin casa. Cand o plimb pe afara mereu se uda. Ii place sa alerge dupa pasari pe camp si daca gaseste un bat mi-l aduce mie, ca sa ne jucam. Cand o mangai, blana ei neagra e moale si inteleg ca acum este fericita in casa noastra.

Uneori mergem in parcul Conroy. Este un parc mare unde cainii se pot juca in voie. E ca o padure si cu luminisuri. Cand mergem acolo, vine si Hunter, care e rapid ca un ghepard. Hunter e cainele unui prieten de-al tatalui meu. Hunter e mai mare decat Roxi si e de aceeasi rasa, Ciobanesc German. Ei se alearga unul pe altul si daca arunci un bat ei se intrec sa-l prinda. De obicei castiga Hunter. Cand observa alti caini alearga spre ei cat de repede pot si incep sa-i miroasa. Cand vrem sa plecam la masin, Roxi trage de lesa spre ceilalti caini si spre masini.In masina se plimba pe locurile din spate si scoate capul pe fereastra. Ea e intotdeauna nerabdatoare cand ajungem acasa.

Mesajul meu pentru cei care doresc sa aibe un animal de casa, este sa fie pregatiti sa aibe grija de el pentru totdeauna. Animalele nu sunt pentru joaca, ele sunt pentru toata viata. Daca te hotarasti azi ca vrei sa iei un animal, tine minte ca va trebui sa ai grija de el, in special de pisoi si catelusi. El iti va
face viata mai fericita. Cand esti trist va veni langa tine sa-l mangai, ca pe un ghemotoc moale si pufos. Dar trebuie sa si inveti ghemotocul sa se aseze, si sa aduca inapoi un obiect. Va fii cu tine pentru mult timp. De asemenea trebuie sa aduni dupa el cand isi face nevoile. El nu poate merge in anumite locuri, cum ar fi unele parcuri si trebuie sa ai griija de el. Daca te gandesti sa-ti iei un catel, gandeste-te ce fel de persoana esti. Daca esti mai lenes ai putea lua un catel potolit, daca esti activ poti lua un catel vioi.

In sfarsit, aceasta este povestirea mea despre cainele meu, Roxi. Sper ca v-a placut.

Language: Romanian
Translated by: ???

My Little Excavator

When I was three, I got a little toy excavator for my birthday. I really liked the excavator. It was striped black and orange; the stripes were slanted about 45 degrees, like you would see on one of those caution signs at the start of medians or beside bridge pillars. It had a long, black arm with an orange scoop. Because I didn't have any excavators or anything like them, I really enjoyed having it. I would play with it and not even share it I liked it so much.

Sadly, the excavator got left outside for a few days. It rained, so the excavator got all muddy and its arm was broken when I found it. I was very unhappy that my favourite toy was broken. After crying for a bit, I decided to ask my Dad to mend it. It took a few weeks for him to respond to my plea. When he did, he fixed the excavator so it was as good as new.

I can't remember how it got broken for a second time, but it did get broken. Again I pleaded for my Dad to fix it. I waited for a bit until my Dad had time to repair it. Once he was done, it looked impeccable and worked perfectly.

Somehow the excavator did not make it from our house on Earlscourt Avenue in Toronto to our present home in Ottawa.

I know I really liked my little toy excavator. I hope whoever found my excavator liked it just as much as I did.

Patrick Saumur, Grade 5 Student

Kur jam kandër treyjes une e kum marr
nje lojne per ditlinde. Une e kam masak
lojnon ime. është e zis the e pertekalt. Une
e kum marr sepce e kum paur ne telivisor
Une e kum masak shum the e kam shum
masak.

Lojna u lander ne balkan : dhe
ka ra shi edhe u lag shum. Tani
une kum kajter per pak the i kam kulsuar
mu na ndreq. Tane per i dit e kai
ndeg lojnën une jam gzuar.

Tani per pes dit u theur apet
dhe babi qm e ka ndriger sepce ka pas
vën për djalin vet.

Kur km shkuar toronto nuk
ka ardher me mua. Dhe nuk e di pse.
e kum hupper.

Ishalla kush e ka xhajter lojnen
e dua shum suker une.

Language: Albanian
Translated by: Veli Selmani, Grade 7 Student

Summer Vacation

During last years summer vacation my family and I went to Thousand Islands, Mont Cascades, and Toronto.

I went to Thousand Island with my friends. At Thousands Island we rode a cruise ship. The cruise ship toured different islands. We could see people as they passed by on their motor boats or when they played near the water on the islands. We had our lunch on the cruise. We gave some food to the people that worked on the ship and they let us have lots of free coffee. Later we fed the sea gulls as they flew by the boat. There was beautiful scenery outside the ship. The islands were slowly passing by as if they floated on the gentle waves.

Mont Cascades Water Park was a blast. I loved the water rides Space River and Black Magic. The ride Proracer was fun too. After Riding on the rides I played in the arcade.

At Paramount Canada's Wonderland we went on the Drop Zone. It felt like I weighed nothing when the seats dropped back to the ground. On Shockwave the seats I sat on went 70 feet in to the air and then turned over 360 degrees. The ride Wild Beast wasn't that scary, but still fun. Same goes for Rage which is a pirate ship ride. On one of the rides, called Swings of the Century, I sat on a swing while it spun around. In Splash Works the Body Blast, Riptide Racer, and the Black Hole were my favourite rides. Whitewater Bay is my favourite wave pool. It was so fun riding the waves.

At Niagara Falls, when I went near the Canadian fall I thought it was raining, but there were no clouds. I realized it was the spray from the fall. I also rode on the boat that takes you near the falls. When I went by the American fall there was spray, but I thought I don't really need the raincoat. Near the Canadian fall I was soaked. The spray was everywhere. I could hardly open my eyes.

It was entertaining looking at different animals at the Toronto Zoo. The African section was my favourite. My favourite animals there were the lions, tigers, zebras, elephants, snakes, and of course the cute monkeys.

At Centreville Amusement Park it wasn't as fun as Paramount Canada's Wonderland, but the rides there were fun too. My favourite were the bumper cars and the ride called Sky Ride which is a sky lift. While riding the Sky Rider you get to see the whole park from the top. It is so beautiful.

Before returning to Ottawa we went to the Canada's National (CN) Tower. I liked the Glass Floor. Standing on the glass was scary, but then I got used to it. A person who works there told us the Glass Floor could support the weight of 14 hippos! The view was also awesome. I could see the SkyDome.

My summer vacation was full of fun. My favourite part was going to Paramount Canada's Wonderland because there are so many fun rides there.

Tarim Shahab, Grade 5 Student

پچھلے سال گرمیوں کی چھٹیوں میں ہم اور ہماری فیملی تھاوزنڈ آئیلینڈ، مونٹیکیسکیڈ اور ٹورنٹو گھومنے گئے۔

تھاوزنڈ آئیلینڈ ہم اپنے دوستوں کے ساتھ گئے۔ وہاں پر ہم لوگ کورزشپ پر بیٹھے۔ کورزشپ نے ہم کو مختلف آئیلینڈ دیکھائے۔ ہم نے لوگوں کو دیکھا جو موٹر بوٹس چلا رہے تھے اور کچھ پانی میں کھیل رہے تھے۔ ہم نے کورزشپ پر لنچ کیا۔ ہم نے کچھ کھانا ان لوگوں کو بھی دیا جو بوٹ شپ پر کام کرتے تھے۔ انھوں نے ہم کو فری کافی دی۔ ہم نے برڈ کو کھانا کھلایا جب وہ بوٹ کے پاس سے گزرے۔ چاروں طرف بہت خوبصورت نظارے تھے۔ ہم لوگوں نے مووی بنائی اور فوٹو کھینچی۔

مونٹ کیسکیڈ میں ہم لوگوں کو بہت مزہ آیا۔ مجھے واٹر رائیڈز، اسپیس ریور اور بلیک میجک پر بہت اچھا لگا۔ رائٹ پرور ریس پر بھی بہت مزہ آیا۔

پیرامائونٹ کینڈ اونڈ رلینڈ میں جب ہم لوگ ڈراپ زون پر بیٹھے جب نیچے کی طرف گیا تو ایسا لگا کہ بالکل بھی وزن نہیں ہے۔ شوک ویو میں جب بیٹھا تو سیٹ ۷ فٹ ہوا میں جا کر گھوم گئی۔ وائڈ بیٹ اور رینج خطرناک نہیں تھا مگر مزہ آیا۔ ایک جھولا جس کا نام تھا سونگ آف دی سینچری تھا اسپر جب میں بیٹھا تو جو لہ چاروں طرف گھوم گیا۔ اسکے علاوہ میں بوڈی بلاسٹ، رپٹائڈ ریسر اور بلیک ہول پر بھی بیٹھا تو بہت مزہ آیا۔

جب ہم نائیگرہ فال گئے تو ہم سمجھے کہ بارش ہو رہی ہے مگر حقیقت میں نائیگرہ فال کا پانی ہم پر اڑ کر آ رہا تھا۔ ہم لوگ بوٹ میں بیٹھے جو ہم کو فال کے قریب لے گئی۔ پاس جانے پر ہم لوگ بالکل بھیگ گئے۔

ہم لوگ ٹورنٹو زو گئے تو وہاں پر ہم لوگوں نے بہت سارے جانوروں کو دیکھا۔ میرا پسندیدہ افریکن سائٹ تھی۔ میرا پسندیدہ جانور شیر، چیتا، زیبرا، ہاتھی، سانپ، اور بندر جو بہت پیارے لگ رہے تھے۔

سینٹرول ویل امیوزمنٹ پارک میں ونڈرلینڈ جیسا مزہ نہیں آیا مگر وہ جھولے وہاں کے اچھے بھی تھے۔ میرے پسندیدہ جھولے بیمر کار اور اسکائی رائڈ تھا۔ جب میں اسکائی رائڈ پر بیٹھا تو اونچائی سے پورا پارک دیکھائی رہا تھا جو کہ بہت خوبصورت لگ رہا تھا۔

آخر میں ہم لوگ سی۔ این ٹاور گئے۔ مجھے گلاس فلور اچھا لگا۔ اس پر کھڑے ہونے سے ڈر لگ رہا تھا۔ ایک آدمی جو وہاں کام کرتا تھا اس نے بتایا کہ گلاس فلور ۱۴ ہپوز کا وزن اٹھا سکتا ہے۔ وہاں کا نظارے بہت اچھا تھا۔

میری گرمیوں کی چھٹیوں میں ہم کو بہت مزہ آیا۔ میری پسندیدہ جگہ پیرامائونٹ کینڈ اونڈ رلینڈ تھا کیونکہ وہاں پر بہت سارے جھولے تھے۔ میں ہمیشہ یاد رکھوں گا۔

Language: Urdu
Translated by: ???

Different Religions

My father and mother have completely different religions. My father is Buddhist and my mother is an Atheist.

Atheism is when you believe there is no god and no second life or reincarnation. My mother is also a Humanist; she believes that you should live life ethically, care for others, and be as honest as possible in your dealings with them.

Buddhism is quite different. In Buddhism there is reincarnation, you have many lives and you have to be respectful and kind in each one to get to a higher life form. If you are disrespectful, you might get a life form that is difficult like a small bug, where you have to work hard to survive as punishment. There are also many different "minds" to develop, some of which are love, patience, and happiness. Eventually, once you have lived many lives, expressed many kindnesses and developed all the minds, you become a Buddha. There is also meditation which lets you empty the mind, which my father does on a regular basis.

My mother and father respect each other's religions even though they are different. My grandmother and grandfather on my mother's side used to be Protestant (like my mother); my grandmother was raised a Baptist, and my grandfather was raised in the United Church. Both of them respect my mother's beliefs, but my grandmother really wanted my mum to get married in a church. My mum and dad did some research and decided to get married in a Unitarian Church. The Unitarians have very broad, open ideas about religion that do not violate my parents' religious beliefs. Getting married in a Unitarian church was a good solution, because it pleased my grandmother but it didn't force my parents to express something that they did not believe.

My grandmother on my father's side is Episcopalian (an American religion that is like Anglicanism in Canada). She respects my father's beliefs. My uncle was a Catholic priest (he wasn't allowed to get married) but he decided not to be. Later he married my aunt, who was raised as an Episcopalian, and he became an Episcopalian priest.

When my aunt got older, she began to celebrate nature by marking special times like the Winter Solstice.

I don't think I am Buddhist or Atheist. I believe that there is a god but he/she/it doesn't have that much control over you and you have to make most of your choices. I like to think that better things will happen to you if you make better choices. I also don't really believe in reincarnation or a second life, but I definitely believe there is some kind of god, and if you pray and make good choices then you will have a good life. I think you should always respect other peoples' religions, even if they are different from yours.

Merissa Taylor-Meissner, Grade 5 Student

나의 아빠와 엄마는 다른 종교를 가지고 있다. 아빠의 종교는 불교이고 엄마의 종교는 아테네이스트 (Atheiet) 이다. 엄마의 종교는 만약 그 종교를 믿으면 신도 두번째 삶도 없다. 나의 엄마는 인간이다. 그녀는 그녀 보다 다른 사람을 먼저 생각하고 노력한다고 해야 한다고 믿고 있다. 하지만 불교는 아주 다르다. 불교는 많은 사람에게 예의 있고 친절 하게 대하며 각각 높고 낮음의 차이가 있다. 만약 내가 예의 없고 불친절 하거나 하면 내 인생은 벌레 같은 작은 인생을 살 것이다. 어떤 일이 힘들어도 참고 좋은 생각만 하며 살아 가는 것이 불교이다. 명상을 할땐 머리를 비우고 우리 아빠는 매일 명상을 한다. 우리 부모님은 각각 자신들의 종교를 존중해 준다. 나의 인가 쪽은 엄마의 종교를 믿고 친가 쪽은 아빠의 종교를 믿는다고 생각 하겠지만 모두 다른 종교를 믿는다. 하지만 언제나 서로를 존중 해 준다. 심지어는 크리스찬 쪽의 종교는 아니지만 교회에서 결혼을 했었을 정도이다. 나는 내가 불교 이거나 아테네이스트 (Atheiet) 라고 생각 하진 않는다. 나는 신 이라는 것이 사람의

마음을 조종하거나 모든 길을 신이 차지 하지
않는 다고 믿는다. 나는 사람이 생각하는 대로
하는 것이 더 나은 방법이라고 생각 한다.
또한 나는 할머니, 할아버지 의 종교는 믿지
않는다. 만약 내가 기도를 하면 내 삶이
좋아진다 라는 종교를 믿진 않지만 나는 언제나
다른 종교를 존중 해주어야 한다고 생각한다.
만약 종교가 다르 더라도 말이다.

Language: Korean
Translated by: Sol Bee Kim, Grade 7 Student

My trip to Normandy

At home we have a picture of my brother and I playing on a beach. It is nothing special unless you know that the picture was taken in Normandy, France at a village called *Courcelles les Mer.* This little town was the center of the Canadian line during the D-day* invasion. My dad took the picture because he thought the idea of 2 Canadian boys playing peacefully (we were flinging mud at each other) on Juno beach 61 years after the actual invasion was cool.

Last summer my family and I went to Europe. The first part of the trip was to stay a couple days in Normandy. My dad and I went to Juno beach (part of the D-day invasion) and I played in the water. We also went to point-du-Hoc (also part of the invasion) it was a place were a lot of German bunkers were and it was high up on a cliff. There are lots of craters were shells had exploded and a few of the bunkers were completely demolished. I also went to the Omaha beach cemetery. There were A lot of graves (something like 3866) The trip was fun and all, but sometimes I wonder what must have been like then…with all the shells exploding and guns shooting…and the noise! I don't know how anybody could have survived.

Stefan Walker, Grade 6 Student

*D-day is the most famous invasion ever. It occurred during World War 2. It is when the allies (U.S, England and Canada and many more) invaded German occupied Normandy (in France).

نورمنڈی کا سفر

میرے گھر میں ایک تصویر ھے جس میں، میں اور میرا بھائ سمندر کے کنارے کھیل
رہے ہیں ۔ اس تصویر میں کوئ خاص بات تو نہیں سوائے اسکے کہ یہ تصویر فرانس
کے ایک چھوٹے سے شہر کی ہے۔ جسکا نام
Courcelles les Mer ہے۔ یہ شہر دوسری جنگ عظیم کے دوران کینیڈا کی فوجوں کا
اڈا تھا۔ میرے والد نے اس بات کو ذھن میں رکھتے ہوئے یہ تصویر اتاری تھی۔
پچھلے سال گرمیوں کی چھٹیوں میں،اور میرے گھر والے یورپ گئے۔ شروع میں ہم
نورمنڈی میں رکے۔ میں اپنے ابو کے ساتھ Juno Beach گیا۔ ہم اس جگہ بھی گئے جہاں
جرمن فوجوں کے مورچے تھے۔اور یہ ایک اونچی پہاڑی پر تھا۔ اس جگہ پر جگہ جگہ
بم پھٹنے کے نشان تھے۔ اور کچھ مورچے تو بلکل تباہ ہو چکے تھے۔ میں Omaha
Beach کے قبرستان بھی گیا۔ وہاں بے شمار قبریں ہیں۔ شاید 3866 کے قریب ۔
مجھے ان جگہوں پر جانا اچھا لگا لیکن میں کبھی سوچتا ہوں کہ جنگ کے دوران کیسا
لگتا ہو گا جب ہر طرف بم پھٹ رہے ہونگے اور افراتفری کا عالم ہو گا۔ مجھے یہ
سمجھ نہیں آتا کہ کوئ اس میں سے کیسے بچ کر نکل سکتا ہے۔

Language: Urdu
Translated by: Tamkeen Pirzada

Plum Blossom, Orchid, Bamboo, and Chrysanthemum

Last year my dad went back to China and brought back some Chinese silk paintings. They were paintings of the plum blossom, orchid, bamboo, and chrysanthemum. My dad said, "Traditionally, many Chinese paintings depict plum blossom, orchid, bamboo, and chrysanthemum as symbols of noble characters."

Inspired by both the beauty and resilience of nature's flora, The Chinese poets and painters have, over the centuries, imbued particular plants and flowers with auspicious meaning, literary resonance, and scholarly virtue. In China, for example, the plum, orchid, chrysanthemum, and bamboo are popularly known as the "Four Gentlemen," or "Four Men of Honor" because they can stand the bitter winter and keep each other's company.

Plum Blossom: The plum blossom is one of the first signs of spring and symbolizes happiness and ethical qualities of strength, a new fortune and constancy in love because of always being one of the first to bloom every year.

Orchid: The pure and elegant orchid, with its subtle fragrance is a rare plant and provides pleasure. It has serene beauty and symbolizes rarity or preciousness.

Bamboo: The bamboo stands sturdy, upright, handsome, and vigorous. It is able to remain fresh and green even in the cold winter months.
The Chinese symbol often used to represent the joints of a bamboo means living a virtuous life. The hollow center of the bamboo also indicates that the scholar, learned yet humble, is able to accept criticism and is open to new ideas.

Chrysanthemum: The Chrysanthemum blooms in the ninth month of the year. It blooms in the midst of frost when other flowers begin to wither. This shows a dignified character. Its strong and colorful blooms show triumph over the adversity.

Gary Wang, Grade 5 Student

梅兰竹菊

Gary Wang

去年我爸爸从中国带回了具有东方特色的几幅丝绸画。它们是梅兰竹菊。我爸爸告诉我：中国艺术家们传统上常以梅兰竹菊作为高雅，顽强的象征。

受大自然花草的美丽及顽强精神的启发，上千年来中国的诗人和画家们借某些花草为主题来赞美人间的道德风尚。历年来，人们一直将梅兰竹菊称为："四君子"。它们每一个都具有理想的孔夫子式学者的高贵品德。

梅

是春天最早开花的花草之一。它象征着幸福和能力，也代表着好运气以及持之一恒的爱情。

兰

它代表着纯洁和雅致。以它独特的清香味为人类和大自然提供一个极为舒适的生活环境。同时

它也代表着稀有和珍贵。

竹

它代表着坚强、少病和青春。在冬季它仍然保持自己的绿色和新鲜。它还象征着生命的正直。它的空心标志着谦虚好学的高尚品德。

菊

一年九个月中它都可以开花。在其它花草枯萎时它仍然开花结果，充分显示了它的顽强的高贵品德。它的坚强和无数的花色也同时说明它与大千世界共生存以及和谐生长的包含精神。

2006年4月17日

Language: Chinese
Translated by: ???

Hawthorne Writes

These are some personal anecdotes (funny, interesting, remarkable, everyday, embarrassing or wonderful things that have happened to me before).

A funny thing happened to me before when I was on a field trip to the Museum of Science and Technology. My class was separated into groups and my group went to the Nortel Networks Play Structure in the centre of the building. When we went down the slide, one of us got stuck. Not knowing that they were stuck, another went in and they got stuck too. Then, I went down and got stuck in there and we tried to get out. Then the last child in our group went down and we were all stuck. I managed to crawl out but I accidentally crawled on someone. After I got out, everybody else came rolling down and we were finally out.

An interesting thing that has happened before was when my family along with 3 other families were invited to go to a lake to fish and swim. I didn't really want to catch fish using a fishing rod so my dad helped me catch fish using nets and a bucket. We filled up the bucket with small fish, medium fish and big fish and then I dumped all the fish back in the lake and then went to eat lunch.

Another interesting thing that happened on that same day was when I caught a fish/ bug. It looked like an ant, spider, lobster and minnow mixed together and it was the size of a marble. It was very weird but someone knocked over the bucket and it swam back into the lake.

Another interesting thing that happened there was when I was searching for frogs and I found one still with a tail, but it accidentally drowned when another frog jumped on top of it and it couldn't breathe. While the frogs were drowning, I decided to fish using a fishing rod and saw a fish the about the size of a laptop that had turned white (including its eyes), lying dead.

I enjoyed these trips and I hope that they happen again or to have new trips someday in the near future.

Tao Wang, Grade 6 Student

霍索恩小学作品

以下记述了一些曾经发生在作者身边的、真实的趣闻轶事（包括一些日常发生在我们中间的、令人捧腹的笑话、趣事，或尴尬窘困的场面）。

记得有一次，我随全班同学去科技博物馆参观游览，曾亲历一件令人可笑的事。当时，全班同学分成若干小组分头游览。我们小组先来到位于展厅中心的北电公司展位。参观完北电的展品后，我和同学们乘坐展位的滑梯下到地上。当第一位同学滑下的时候，不知何种原因，被卡在了滑梯的底部。后面的同学不知道前面发生的情况，争恐后地滑了下来，而且也都一个又一个地被卡住，摔倒在一起。我自己经历也和他们一样。由于大家都像叠罗汉似地压在一起，我只能从堆里爬出来。其间，还不小心踩到其他人。最后，我们都一个地滚爬着，来到了滑梯下。看着大家滑稽的样子，我们都哈哈大笑起来。

一次，我们全家同另外三家一起应邀去位于魁北克省的一个大湖钓鱼、游泳，我遇到了一件让我终难以忘怀的趣事。我不会，也希望用钓鱼竿钓鱼。于是，我老爸就和我一道用一马提混出标本的网子捉鱼。那湖里的鱼儿很好捉，我们很快就捉了很多，有大有小，装满了一小桶。午餐准备好了，我把捉到的鱼全都放回到湖里，然去吃午饭。

同一天，我还碰到另外一件离奇而有趣的事。我捉到了一个奇特的小动物。我之所以用"一个"，是因为它可能是一条鱼，也可能是一虫子。它看起来既像蚂蚁，又有些像蜘蛛，龙虾或用作诱饵小鱼，有一马玻璃弹珠那么大。它是那样的古怪，我们都感到非常惊奇。最后，小桶被一个朋友不小心不並番倒，那个小生物很快地消失在汪洋湖水里了。

那天午饭后，我和朋友去捉青蛙。我发观一马小青蛙，它的尾巴还没有完全蜕掉，但並坊被另外一马大青蛙跳落在背上，多倍沉入水底，而逃跑了。这时，我拿起钓竿准备的鱼咪，发观水底还沉着一条比计祢机星器那么大的鱼。它已经死了很久了，整个身体和眼身青都已经发白了。

我非常参加这样的一日游学活动。它不仅使我们暂时从单沉闷的日常生活中摆脱出来，而且使我们的生活更加充实，书富多我期待着在不久的将来再次参加这样的活动。

Language: Chinese
Translated by: ???

Visiting Washington D.C.

In the Summer Break of 2005, my family and I went on a tour traveling to New York, Philadelphia and Atlantic City. But the most rememberable place we went to was the grand state of Washington DC.

I was really looking forward to going there and discovering, in real life all the spectacular places people talked about seeing. Washington DC was a *famous* state; I could almost imagine kings and queens casually roaming along the streets! Not that the president - the person that basically *controlled* the United States – didn't live there.

Washington was essentially what I expected. There was fine architecture everywhere and I couldn't even *imagine* living there. Think: passing something as lordly as the Washington Monument or the *White House* going to school everyday!

First, there was the White House. The first thing I thought when I saw it was: *Wow! Such a wonderful building could've been ruined on September 11th!* Yes, I know this wasn't the greatest thing to think when you're looking at such a royal edifice that the president currently inhabited but I couldn't help myself! Just try and imagine, while you're gazing out at the White House, a plane coming in and crashing into such an exquisite building! Think of all the history that could be erased! The *legendary* George Washington had lived there! Well, I guess you have to see it in real life to truly realize what you're about to demolish.

But enough with that; though, before I continue, I'll take a moment to remember the people that prevented the destruction of the White House – the passengers on the plane *Flight 93*.

The next place we went to was the Lincoln memorial. Upon entering, the main focus point is the huge statue right in the center of the memorial. And of course, you could guess right away that it was indeed Abraham Lincoln. Then I discovered that there were two walls covered in inscriptions. After reading them carefully, I concluded that it was probably the story of how the United States of America came to be and the role of which Abraham Lincoln took in it.

I could sense all the effort put into carving the inscriptions and making the statue – even though the memorial was actually never completed. I thought to myself: Lincoln was a great man; he stood up for what he believed: he changed lives and deserved much honor.

The final place I will mention is the Korean War Memorial. In the memorial, there was a replication of a battle ground; there were soldiers that looked almost real from their poses and facial expressions, the wounded and the able. The artist portrayed the looks of bravery and true determination/ambition on the soldiers.

There was also a fountain made in memory of all the soldiers in the war, carved for all the soldiers that had died, gone missing or survived the war. This was accompanied by a huge wall carved with all the names of the soldiers. The wall surprised me of how the soldiers were commemorated so well: someone took the time to carve *all* the names of the soldiers on a stone block. I guess hard work really does pay off.

I thought this trip was very interesting and I learned a lot from it. The memories will last a lifetime, the monuments will too. I hope everyone can visit Washington someday too and enjoy the memories the city has to offer.

Nicole Wang, Grade 6 Student

Suvi 2005, minu pere, ja mina läksime New Yorki, Philadelphiai ja Atlanta Citysse. Kõige toredam koht kuhu me läksime oli Washington DC.

Mul oli väga tore ette kujutada kuidas kuningad jalutasid Valge maja. Washington oli nagu ma ootasin. Igal pool olid imelised ehitised, ja ma ei saaks ette kujutada kuidas ma elaks seal. Mõtle - kooli minnes mööda minnu White Houseist!

Kui ma nägin White House'i, siis mõtlesin et see maja võiks Volla purustatud september 11'is. Kõik see võimas ajalugu! George Washington isegi enne elas seal.

Järgmine koht mida külastasime oli Lincoln memorial. Ma austasin Abraham Lincoln'i väga palju, sest ta seisis ülesa sellele millele ta uskus.

Viimane koht millest räägin teile on Korean War Memorial. Oli kästi suur replica lahingust, ja kõik näo väljendused oli näha. Seal oli üks pursk-kaev mälestuseks kai. Suure seina peale oli sisse kraabitud surnute nimed, mina arvates oli see väga kaval viis et mälestada neid.

Keegi võttis aega et kõik langenute nimed sisse kraapib marmori sisse. Nüüsiis kõva töö ikkagi tasub ära.

Minuarvates, see sõit oli väga huvitav, ja ma õppisin nii rahulikult palju. Need mälestused jäävad mulle eluks ajaks, ja memooriaid jaavad kah. Ma loodan et kõik saaksid külastada Washingtoni, ja ise tunda kui erakordne see oli mulle.

Language: Estonian
Translated by: Jaan Altosaar, Grade 8 Student

My Yu-Gi-Oh Collection

Four years ago I started to collect Yu-gi-oh cards. I started on my seventh birthday when my best friend, Evan, gave me my first pack with my first card, Trial of Nightmare. Yu-gi-oh is a game of luck and strategy. There's also an animated TV series based on the game. From the day I got my first card to this day I have been collecting them. Now I have eight hundred and forty-eight cards. There are different values of cards: common (commonly seen), rare (uncommon), ultimate rare (hard to get), secret rare (few have it), and limited edition (a limited number of them). I have ten limited edition cards. My cards are special to me because I've had them for almost four years.

Once, my best cards went through the wash. Some were destroyed, but some came out all right. Somebody stole a card from me, Black Luster Soldier-Envoy of the Beginning, so as you can see a lot of bad the things happened to my cards, but I'm still happy with the ones I've got.

Matthew Wiley, Grade 5 Student

四年以前我開始了收到 Yu-Gi-oh 卡片，我的開始在

我的第七個生日，我的最好的朋友，Ean，給了我第一

副牌，和 Trial of Nightmare。Yu-Gi-oh 有幸運的戰

術，在電視卡通节目里播放，到現在我仍然收

Yu-Gi-oh 卡片一共八百四十八個卡。這卡有好多種有普通

的，有稀少的，有好極段的，有秘密的，有限制的散本。我有十

個有限制的散本。這些卡好特別我已經保存了三四年。

有一回我最好的卡放进了洗衣机里經过溶洗有一些破懷

有一回有人偷了我的卡"起點的黑久色，澤戰士俠於節，现

在，你知道了有關我的卡，我仍然好快樂我有

這些卡。

Language: Chinese
Translated by: Colin Wu, Grade 8 Student

What are we doing?

Sometimes I wonder why we are doing certain things. Have you ever wondered that? Why we kill, why we start wars, why we fight and yell over something as small as who is right about something you read...

When I say "kill", I know you probably think of guns, knives, and all of those horrible things we use for committing that retched crime. And the other thing you think about are the cold, still bodies of...Hold on, the bodies of what? Humans, animals, or plants? Okay, so you draw the line there. After all, cutting down plants and trees is not, and never has been, a crime, right? Who could possibly care about something like that? We have so much. So just how long will that last? Maybe a couple of centuries. How many trees were cut down in the last ten minutes? A million, a billion, more? I am not exaggerating, merely stating facts that most people know, and ignore.

We sit here, working or playing on the computer, watching television, eating, sleeping, and completely ignoring everyone who says things like this. We lock ourselves away, pretending that if we go to school, or go to our little jobs, then when we die we are going to be so proud of the undistinguished lives we lived. We say to ourselves that there is no point, or no time to go running around after little things like the forests.

Well, what about the rainforests? When cute little kindergarteners think about the rainforests, they think about toucans and frogs living in a dense, leafy terrain. How many adults would care to tell them that people are hacking the rainforest down to build pastures for cows, which are going to be turned into hamburgers for fast food restaurants? We humans, the superior beings, shall not be troubled by such inferior things. And if you protest, say that I am not being fair, that you do care about the rainforests, then why are you not doing anything?

Tons of animals live in the rainforests, and we cut their homes down. Perhaps not you in particular, but I can be almost positive that you are not "chomping at the bit" to help those who were there first. Sure, if you never do anything, it will not affect you. It will affect everybody that comes after you. In future generations, some little child will look at their parent and ask why you did not help, did not preserve the environment so that they could see it in all of it's' glory. And that poor parent will have to say "I don't know", or "They never really thought it would come to this". The child might even ask if things were ever like this, looking at some forgotten picture book. If there were enough wood to make picture books.

Fantasy books, my favourite kind, almost always have another world in them. Why? So many wonderful books are filled with tales of dense forests, rainforests included. Are we not pleased with the world we live in? Of course not. Why should we be pleased with a world filled with pollution, and terrible things happening that scroll across our conscience when ever we have spare time? I love to write fantasies, and the worlds I place inside are never some kind of high-tech, modern world. I know friends who, given the choice, would love to talk about all of the "cool" inventions that are to come with the future. However, it makes me shudder to think that most of these will be a futile attempt to keep humanity alive and well.

I know every one has the right to say they are proud of who they are. I cannot see any reason to argue with that. What I am asking is if you are pleased with the acts of humanity as a whole.

I know that there are always those who will say what we are doing is right. I know that my point of view may be "immature" and that I am not currently doing anything myself to help anyone.

The truth is I very simply can not.

The truth is you could.

I know several people will be laughing like they hardly ever do right now, saying that I myself am using up the precious rainforest, writing and printing this on paper. However, while doing so, I hope to raise your, and perhaps many others awareness, of all the things we are doing, and that they can help. I can only hope my "immature" opinion counts for going somewhere other than in one ear, out the other. If it has, I do not necessarily mean you have to go marching up to some place and wave signs around. You could just tell more people, or talk about it with a friend. Maybe you could even give a small donation, or even a large one, to help an endangered species, or the rainforest, or others like you…and by doing so, help yourself. It is your choice, and I hope that I have helped by writing this. This is all I can do.

The rest is up to you.

Olivia Williams, Grade 5 Student

ᐃᓛᓐᓇᒃᑯ ᐃᑯᒪᖅᑲᑦᑕᕿᓚ ᖃᓄᐃᓪᓗ
ᐱᓂᕆᐊᒃᓴᖅᑲᖅᑲᑦᑕᒪᒫᖓᑦ, ᐊᖅᐹᕆᓐᓂᑦᑐᓂ.
ᐃᑯᒪᖅᑲᑦᑕᕆᓗᒪᓂ ᑕᐃᒪᓐᓇ? ᖃᓄᐃᓪᓗ ᑐᖅᑯᑦᑎᖅᑲᑦ-
ᒫᖓᑦᑕ, ᖃᓄᐃᓪᓗ ᐅᓇ ᑕᑦᔪᕆᐊᖅᑲᑦᑕᕐᒫᖓᑦᑕ,
ᖃᓄᐃᓪᓗ ᐅᓇ ᑕᖅᑲᑦᑕᕐᒫᖓᑦ ᑐᓱᑦᑐᑎᖅᑲᑦᑕᕐᒫᖓᑦ
ᑲᐱᒪᕈᖅᓴᐊ ᐊᒻᒪ ᐅᖕᐱᕐᓂᖅ ᐱᑦᑐᒍ....

ᑐᖅᑯᑦᑎᓂᖅᒥᑦ ᐅᖅᑲᐅᔪᖅᑳᖅᐸᓚ, ᖄᐅᔾᔭᒪᔭᕚ
ᐃᑯᒪᖅᑲᖅᑲᑦᑕᖅᑐᒃᓴᐅᓯᔪ, ᖁᐱᐅᑎᓂ, ᓴᓂᓐᖏ
ᐊᒻᒪ ᖁᓂᐊᓇᕐᕆᑐᐊᓘᓂ ᕿᑐᕐᖓ ᑎᑭᑦᔪᑎᓪᓚ-
ᑎᓪᓗᓂ ᐱᖕᖓᓂᖅᑐᑦ. ᐊᒻᒪ ᐊᔾᔨᕆ
ᐃᑯᒪᕆᔭᒃᓴᑎᓴᑎ ᓂᓚᓈᖅᑐᐊᓗᐃ, ᑎᒥᖏᓂ-
ᐊᓗᐃ.... ᐅᐊᑦᑎᐊᕈ ᐊᐃ; ᑭᑯ ᑎᒥᖏᓐᕆᑦ?
ᐃᓄᖏᓂ, ᓂᕐᔨᖏᓂ, ᐅᓕᓘᓂ ᐱᕈᖅᔪᐊᖑᕐᓂ?
ᑖᕋᓂ ᓄᖅᑲᖅᑐᑦᑐᒍ. ᓇᑲᑎᓄᓂᖅ ᐱᕈᔪᐊᓂ
ᓗ ᐸᖅᑐᓂ ᐱᖅᓴᓇᐅᓇᐅᖅᔪ ᒪᓐᕆᖑᖅ ᐊᐃ?
ᑭᓇ ᑕᒃᑯᓐᓇᓗ ᐃᒃᐱᒍᑯᒃᑲᓴᖅᐸ? ᑕᒪᒃᑯᓐᓇᓗ
ᐊᒥᖁᓂ ᐃᑯᑲᓴᖅᐸ ᑭᓇ? ᐊᒥᖁᓂ ᐱᖅᑲᖅᐳᒍ.
ᖃᓄᖅ ᐊᑯᓂᐅᐱᐅᓚᓴᖅᐸ? ᐃᓪᓕᖅᑲ ᐊᖅᖁ
ᖁᓕ ᐅᓚᑕᓅᓐᓂ. ᖃᔫᑉ ᓇᐹᖅᑐᐃ
ᓘᑲᑎᖅᑕᐅᖅᑲᐅᑉ ᓚᓐᓴᖅ? ᐊᒥᖁᓚᕆᐅᓗᐃ.
ᔪᓕᐊᓗᐊᑐᐃᓐᓇᕆᑦᑐᓚ, ᑕᒪᒃᑯ ᑯᓗᔪ ᐊᒥᖁᓄ
ᐃᓅᓄ ᐊᓈᑕᐅᔨᒪᔪᑦ.

ᐅᓪᓗ ᐃᖅᑰᕐᓂᖓᓂᑦᑕ ᐃᖅᑲᓇᐃᔭᕐᓂᑦᑕ ᐅᓪᓗᒧᖓ
ᐱᖑᐊᕐᓂᖏᓐᓂᑦᑕ ᖃᓄᖅᐅᓯᕆᓂᓐᓂᑦᑕ, ᑖᕐᓇᔭᕐᖏᑦᑐᖕᓂ,
ᓯᓇᓃᑦᑕ, ᓴᓂᖓᓂᑦᑕ ᐊᓯᖅᑯᓕᑦᑐᑎᒍ ᐃᓄᐃ
ᐅᖅᑳᓚᒃᑯᑦ. ᒪᑐᐃᓂᑦᑕ ᐅᕐᓂᖓ, ᖃᐅᔨᕙᒌᒍ-
ᒃᓂᑦᑕ ᐃᒻᒪᖅᑲ ᖃᐅᑖᒪ ᑕᐃᒪᓐᓇ ᐃᓅᓗᑦᑕ
ᖃᐅᑕᒫᔪᐱᑎᒍ ᐊᑐᕐᓗᑎᒍ, ᐅᕙᑦᑎᓐᓂ
ᐅᐱᒋᓛᖅᒐᑦᑕ ᐊᑑᑎᖃᓚᐅᕐᒥᓂᑦᑎᓐᓂ ᐅᖅᑯᓕᑦᑕ.
ᐅᕙᑦᑎᓐᓂ ᐅᖅᑲᐅᔪᖅᑳᑦᑕᒐᑦᑕ ᓱᕙᑭᐊᖅ, ③ ᐃᓱᓕᓐᓂ-
[illegible] ② ᑕᒪᒃᑯᓂᖓᑦᑎᑦᓯᑯ [illegible] ① ᓇᐹᑦᑐᓃᒃ
ᐅᖂᔪᖅᓴᐊᒥ ᓇᐹᑦᑐᓇ ᐱᕈᖅᓯᐅᔪᒪᔪᑦ
ᓄᓇᖕᒎᑦᑕᑭᐊ? ᐃᓕᓃ ᐊᓕᓴᖅᑐᒍᓄᐃ
ᓴᒪᑐᒥᖕᒐ ᑐᓴᕈᑎ, ᐃᑭᓚᐅᓴᑐᐃ ᓂᖅᔪᑎᓂ
ᐃᒪᖅᓯᒥᐅᑕᐃ, ᐱᕈᔪᐊᖅᔪᐊᓂᖕᓄ ᖅᑲᖕᓄᓇ
ᐊᕐᓚᔭᖅᑲᓇ ᐅᖅᑲᐅᓯᐅᑰᓀᓴᔭᕐ ᑕᒪᒃᑯᐊ
ᓴᐹᖅᑐᐃ ᓇᑲ ᑭᖅᑕᐅᔪ ᓯᕐᓄᓂᖅᔪᓂᓚᐅᔮᖅᑎ
ᐃᖖᔪᐅᒐᓄ, ᐃᖖᔪᐅᒐᐃ ᓂᖅᑭᓴᑲᐊᖑᑐᐊᓀᓂ-
ᓱᖅᑎᓐᑐᑎ ᓂᓇᓂᒐᓃ? ᐅᓗ ᐃᓅᒃᑎᒍ
ᐊᐅᓚᓐᑎᖃᐅᖁᒍ, ᐃᑭᓚᑦᑐᑎᖅᑳᔭᕐᒥᓚᒍ ᑕᒪᒃᑯᓂᖓ
ᒥᖁᓂᖅᓯᓂ. [illegible]
ᓴᑐᕈᖅᑲᑎᓕᒃᓂᑦᑕ ᑐᓯᑦᑕᐅᓇᖁᒃᑯᑦ, ᐅᖅᑲᓂᑕᓄ
ᓵᓪᓚᒋᐊᕆᑦᑐᓂᐅᒪ, ᐃᒃᐱᒍᓱᑦᑎᐊᕈᓇ ᑕᖅᑯᒥᖕᒐ
ᖅᑯᖅᔪᐊ [illegible] ᐃᒪᖅᓯᐅ ᔫᑦ ᓇᐹᖅᑐᖅᑲᖅᓂᖕᒐ,
ᑲᓇᐃᓪᓕ ᖅᑲ ᓄᐃᓴᐳᑎᒥᖕᓂᒃᐱᒃ?

ᑯᓐᓂᖓ ᐃᑲᔪᕐᓂᕐᒥᑎᐊᓪᓚᕆᒃᑲᓚ.
ᑯᓐᓂᖓᓐᓇ, ᐱᖕᓂᖅ ᐃᖕᖏᐅᓯᑎ ᐃᑲᔪᕐᓂᖅᓯᓂ.

ᖃᐅᔨᒪᔪᓐᓇ ᐊᒥᓱᐃ ᐃᓐᓇᕐᓴᖅᑐᖅ; ᐅᖃᓪᓚ
ᓚᕐᑐᒥ ᐊᑐᖅᑐᓐᓇ ᑕᒪᑐᒥᓐᓇ ᑎᑎᕋᖅᑐᓐᓇ
ᐃᓚᐅᔪ. ᐃᓪᓕᓐᓇ ᑕᒪᖕᓇ ᑐᓴᖃᐅᖅᓯᓕᕆᐊᕐᑕᕐ
14 ᐃᑉᐱᒍᔪᓐᓇᕐᐸᓐᓇᕐᓱᖅᑐᖅ ᐃᑲᔪᕐᓚᓂᖅᑕᕐᓄᑦ.
ᒧᑎᖃᓂ ᓯᕐᑭᑎᓯᓇᐊᓗᖅᑐᖅ. ᐃᓐᓇᓐᓂ ᐅᖅᑲᖃᑕᕐᓂ
ᓚ ᐃᔪᒪᔪᓐᓂ ᐅᖅᑲᖅᑲᑎᖅᑲᓐᓄᑎ. ᐃᓪᓕᖅᑲ
ᐅᖅᑐᒥ ᑐᓂᔪᐊᕐᓄᑎ ᐊᓐᓂᕆᔪᒥᓐᓄᓐ. ᐃᑲᔪᕐᑎᒥ
ᓚᖅᑐᓂ, ᐃᑲᔪᖅᑐᐃᑲᓂᕐᔪᕐᓄᑎ. ᐃᔪᒪᖅᔪᖅᑐᑎ
ᐃᒪᑐ ᐃᑲᔪᖅᑐᐃᖕᓇ ᑕᒪᖕᓇ ᑎᑎᕋᖅᑲᑦ
ᑕᐃᒪᖕᓇᑐᐊ ᐃᑲᔪᕐᓇᖅᑲ
ᐊᔪᐊ ᐃᓅᖃᔪᐊᓂ

Language: Inuktituk
Translated by: Kim Kangok

My Trip to China

At last, after 6 years of waiting, I was finally going back to my homeland, China. I waited for the glorious moment when I would hear these wonderful words: "Pack your suitcase, we're taking a trip to China."

For nearly 6 years I had not seen my grandparents, my aunt and uncle, and other important relatives in my family. Twice, my mom's parents came to see us in Canada, but going back just wasn't the same. They saw our new house and everything, but I was going back to where my childhood had started, where everything for me began. This was very important to me because I could know more about my background and my culture.

When I arrived in China, I saw my grandparents, aunts, and uncles, waiting for my mom and I with big smiles on their faces. They had the fresh homemade look that could brighten every single unhappy memory in my life. We quickly got out of the airport and went to a restaurant where we could have dinner. They ordered at least 10 dishes. (They were great dishes you know, with crab and lobster and other expensive stuff.) I was stunned. Rarely in Canada we could have such a great dinner. I was very touched, and it was not the dishes that made me feel that way, it was the thought.

After the dinner, we went back home. As soon as I entered the apartment, I could smell the fresh smell of home. All of (Well, most of them.) my childhood pictures were still there! My grandparents still had preserved them. It seemed like that every single memory I had belonged here. I flopped on my bed and refreshed my mind of what it was like back in the olden days.

In China, my grandparents accompanied me to almost every single place that I wanted to be. (You can't go alone outside in China. There's lots more criminals there.) And I was so happy that they did. They are older, and they cared for me so much. They bought me lots of stuff, (I didn't ask for a lot.) they taught me all they knew, they made me wonderful homemade meals, and they just really cared for me.

My trip to China was a great trip. It was educational, and I got to see all of my relatives. I was heartbroken the day I had to leave to come back to Canada. I might be another long time before I could see some of these people again. Now just the pictures that I have of this trip can really remind me of how much my grandparents cared for me during this trip, whether it's only me or if it's with my relatives. But I was also happy to come back to Canada again so I could share some of these memories and adventures I had in China, with people like you.

Jingru Zhang, Grade 5 Student

Mi Viaje a La China

Por fin, después de seis años de espera, regresaría a mi país de nacimiento. Esperaba por ese momento glorioso en que oiría estas palabras maravillosas: 'Tienes que hacer la maleta, vamos a la China.'

No había visto a mis abuelos, a mis tíos ni tampoco a otros parientes importantes durante casi seis años. Dos veces, los padres de mi mamá nos habían visitado aquí en Canada, pero eso nunca sería iqual a un viaje a mi patria. Iba a volver al lugar donde se empezó mi niñez, el principio de mi vida. Este viaje iba a ser muy importante para mí porque iba a descubrir mucho en cuanto a mi cultura y a mi origen.

Cuando llegué en la China, vió a mis abuelos y a mis tíos en el aeropuerto esperandonos a mí y a mi madre con sonrisas muy grandes. Tenían esa apariencia sana y fresca que podía mejorar a todos mis recuerdos malos. Salimos rápido del aeropuerto y fuimos a comer en un restaurante cercano. Pidieron por lo menos diez platos distintos que raras veces se podían encontrar en Canada: cangrejo, langosta y otros platos caros. Todo esto me dejó atónita y emocionada a la vez. No fue la comida que me hizo sentir así, fue la intencion.

Duespués de cenar, fuimos a la casa de mis abuelos. El momento en que entré en el apartamento, podía oler el olor fresco del hogar. Todas mis fotos de niñez estaban allí. Mis abuelos se las habían mantenidos. Me parecía que cada recuerdo que tenía estaba aquí. Me dejé caer en la cama y me refresqué de todas mis recuerdos de los días dorados de mi niñez.

En la China, no se puede vagar solo por las calles a causa de la alta tasa de delincuencia. Entonces, mis abuelos me acompañaban a cada lugar que querría visitar. Mis abuelos me cuidaban muy bien. Me compraron muchas cosas, sin que yo les pida, me enseñaron todo lo que sabían y me cocinaron comidas deliciosas.

Mi viaje a la China fue memorable. Fue educativo y podía ver a todos mis parientes. Con el corazón roto, volví a Canada. Iba a ser otro largo tiempo antes de que viera a algunos de estas personas de nuevo. Ahora las fotos de mi viaje me hacen recordar de la ternura de mis

abuelos. A la vez, estaba feliz volver a Canada para compartir algunos de mis recuerdos con gente como ustedes.

Language: Spanish
Translated by: Kelly Stanutz-Sedlar, Intermediate Teacher and Sarah Beale,
Grade 8 Student

Hawthorne *Writes*
because everyone has a story...

1. French – Français

French

French is spoken by over 64 million people around the world. Most of these people live in France. It is also spoken in Canada, Côte d'Ivoire, and Haiti to name a few countries.

Canada is recognized as an official bilingual country. However, only 24 percent of Canadians speak French as their mother tongue and most of them live in the province of Québec.

There are two types of French spoken in Canada: Acadian French from New Brunswick and French-Canadian also known as Québécois French. Because of Canada's history, the French spoken in Canada is quite different from the French one might hear in France. Most of the original settlers came from parts of France other than Paris who spoke French from the "Ancien Régime". For this reason, the French vocabulary and pronunciation heard in Canada is very unique and distinctive to the rest of the French speaking world.

Français

Le Français est parlé par plus de 64 millions de personnes dans le monde. La majorité d'entre eux habitent en France. On parle aussi le français au Canada, en Côte d'Ivoire et en Haïti pour nommer quelques pays.

Le Canada a deux langues officielles : le français et l'anglais. Par contre, seulement 24 pourcents des canadiens parlent français comme langue première et la majorité de ceux-ci habitent dans la province de Québec.

Il y a deux genres de français parlé au Canada : le français Acadien du Nouveau-Brunswick et le français Canadien du Québec. À cause de notre histoire, le français parlé au Canada est très différent du français que l'on parle en France. La plupart des colons son venus de la France mais pas de la région de Paris. Ces colons parlaient un français de « l'Ancien Régime ». Pour cette raison et plusieurs autres, le vocabulaire et la prononciation utilisés au Canada sont très uniques et distincts pour le reste du monde de la francophonie.

Language Description and Translation by: Richard Smith, French Teacher

My Grandmother's Quilt

This quilt was started by my father's mother, Margaret Reynolds, and my mother, Hazel McSweeney Broad-Head, when she was expecting her first baby. It would have taken many, many hours to cut each piece, arrange the pattern, and sew them together. Much like this project we are starting at Hawthorne.

I like to imagine what these ladies may have talked about as they worked on it over the months. Did they hope for health and happiness for the grandchild on the way? Complain about the weather or the price of milk? Did they share stories of when their families first came to Canada?

Can you imagine that they would think for just the tiniest minute, that over sixty years later, Margaret's great granddaughter would sit in a school that in so many ways resembles this quilt?

Stretch your imagination just a little further and start thinking of this quilt in the way I am. Think to yourself that each of the pieces of fabric has not come from different dresses but from different countries and nations from around the world.

Can you see how they could represent a different culture background or language? Could there be a bit of you or your family in there?

It took over 500 diamond shaped pieces to create the star. They are mixed fabrics and designs and yet they all work together. Each piece is important to the quilt, just like each of you are important to our school, our community, and to all our lives.

As you work on your assignment, I hope you celebrate your unique contribution that will help produce this school project that is so like my grandmother's quilt.

Sharron Mahon, Co-Chair Hawthorne School Council

Cette couverture piquee etait commence par ma grandemere paternel, Margaret Reynolds et ma mère, Hazel McSweeney Broadhead, quand elle etait enceinte avec son premier bébé.

Comme ce projet de Hawthorne, « Hawthorne Writes », ça pris beaucoup des heures a couper chaque morceaux matériel, les arrangées avec le motif. Apres, il faut tous les coudre.

J'aime imaginer, ce que les femmes ont discute pendant qu'elles travaillent avec la couverture piquée depuis les mois. Est-ce qu'elles espéraient pour la santé et le bonheur du bébé qui vient ? Est-ce qu'elles se plaignent de la température, or le prix du lait ? Est-ce qu'elles partageaient des histoires familiale, de leur rendez-vous au Canada ?

Pouvez vous imaginer ce que Margaret Reynolds et ses amies pensaient à une école qui semble à une grande couverture piquée ? Par un effort d'imagination, pensez à cette couverture, comme moi. Chaque morceau de matériel, ne vient pas des robes, mais de différents pays autour du monde. Des cultures, des langues et des coutumes de diversité innombrable . . . voyez vous votre pays d'origine dedans la mosaïque de la couverture ?

Au moins cinq cent morceau de diamant, ma grande maman et ses amies ont coudre pour faire l'étoile au milieu de la couverture. Les étoffes sont de différents desseins, mais ils se sont bien effectifs.

Chaque morceau de la couverture est important, aussitôt que chaque étudiant et personne qui ont des liens avec la communauté, l'école Hawthorne et a tous nos vies.

Quand tu écris ton histoire, j'espère que tu vas célébrer votre contribution unique qui aide à produire ce projet magnifique à l'école Hawthorne.

Language : French
Translated by : Tracey Heard

My Treasure

My treasure is a toy motor boat. We and one of our neighbors helped make it. It's red all over the top and blue all over the bottom. We got it at the basement. I love my treasure because we made it ourselves and no one else has one like it and it has a bright light!

Jeremy Boyd, Grade 1 Student

Mon Trésor

Mon trésor est un jouet, c'est un bateau avec moteur. Nous avons construit le bateau avec notre voisin. Le bateau est rouge partout en haut, et bleu en bas. On a eu le bateau à mon sous-sol. J'aime mon trésor parce que on a fabriqué le bateau nous même et que personne a le même chose que nous!

Language: French
Translated by: ???

Childhood accidents!

Childhood accidents, we've all experienced them, we all have memories of them, and there is usually a lesson to be learned. This story is about a girl whose life was turned around by carelessly riding her bike across the street. This is what happened…

It was a bright Monday morning and Nancy had just finished riding her bike through the park with her friends. She stopped at the curb before crossing the street and saw a car that was heading towards her. She thought that because she was on a bike, that she could make it across the street before the car came near her. She was wrong.

As she started crossing the road her shoelace got stuck in the chain and she stopped in the middle of the road. She made it half way across the road, then the car started speeding up. Her shoelace was still stuck in the chain and she could not move. The car started coming closer and closer, until it hit her. She went flying headfirst into the bumper and was knocked unconscious. Her friends picked her up off the road and ran home to call 911.

When she got home her parents checked her head out and only found a little cut by her ear. It was just a little cut so her parents did not bother taking her to the hospital.

A few weeks later her hearing started to go. Her parents took her to the hospital and it turned out that the tiny little cut on the side of her ear had damaged her hearing and from then on she would have to wear hearing aids.

That was not the only accident that Nancy got into. When she was about 12 years old she was playing hide and go seek with about 80 other kids on her block. She had found the perfect hiding spot behind some big metal doors at the park. Someone found her hiding and they grabbed a hold of the door.

While my mother held onto the door, using it to help her up, her friend let go of the door, and it smashed the tips of her fingers. She felt a sharp pain go through the tips of her fingers. She ran with her friends from the park through a football stadium where people were playing. All the players were starring at her hand. She didn't understand why they were starring at her, so she looked down at her hand and saw that the tip of her finger was missing. I guess when the door smashed closed it cut off the tip of her finger.

Her friends ran home to call 911. They arrived at the hospital in less then five minutes, the doctor looked at her hand and she had to get stitches and keep a bandage on for about a year.

There was also another accident Nancy got into. She was outside with her friends hanging out. They were climbing a tree in front of one of their friend's houses. She made it to the top and sat on the branch. The branch that she was holding onto snapped, she fell off and landed flat on her back. Once again her friends had to bring her home and she had to go to the hospital to get checked out. It turns out that none of her bones were broken, but she did damage her arm.

Nancy got into a lot of accidents in her life; I'm surprised she actually made it to the age of Forty-one. I mean, she got hit by a car, lost part of her finger, and was unconscious a few times. Nancy is my mom and if she was not here right now I would not be alive. She could have really gotten hurt. That is why each time when I cross the road I look both ways and if a car is coming I wait until it passes.

Kayla Talbot, Grade 7 Student

Les accidents de l'enfance

Nous avons tous souvenirs des accidents qui remontent à notre enfance. On peut habituellement en tirer une leçon. Le récit qui suit est celui d'une fille qui a vu sa vie chambardée à cause d'un accident de bicyclette, alors qu'elle traversait la rue sans faire attention. Voici son histoire ...

C'était un lundi matin ensoleillé et Lindy venait juste de faire du vélo dans le parc avec ses amies. Elle s'est arrêtée dans la courbe avant de traverser la rue et a vu une voiture qui se dirigeait vers elle. Elle pensait qu'à vélo, elle pourrait vite traverser avant que l'auto ne vienne. Elle se trompait.

Comme elle avançait dans la rue, son lacet s'est pris dans la chaîne et elle a dû s'arrêter au milieu de la rue. Alors qu'elle était à mi-chemin, la voiture s'est mise à accélérer. Son lacet était toujours dans l'engrenage de la chaîne et l'empêchait de bouger. La voiture se rapprochait et se rapprochait jusqu'à ce qu'elle la frappe. Elle a été projetée sur le pare-chocs, tête première et a perdu connaissance. Ses amies l'ont enlevé de la rue et ont couru à la maison pour appeler le 911.

Une fois à la maison, ses parents ont examiné sa tête et ont seulement trouvé une petite coupure près de l'oreille. Comme ce n'était qu'une coupure mineure, ses parents n'ont pas jugé nécessaire de l'emmener à l'hôpital.

Après quelques semaines, son ouïe
commençait à diminuer.
Ses parents l'ont mené à l'hôpital
et ont appris que la petite
coupure s'était reliée et que
désormais, elle devrait porter
un appareil auditif.

Ce n'était pas l'unique
accident dont Lindy devait
souffrir. Quand elle avait envi-
ron douze ans, elle jouait à cache-
cache avec quelques 80 enfants
du coin où elle habitait. Elle
avait trouvé la cachette idéale
derrière de grosses portes de
métal au parc. Quand on l'a
découvert, quelqu'un a tenu
l'une des portes.

Pendant que ma mère tenait
l'autre porte pour sortir de sa
cachette, son amie a lâché l'autre porte et celle-ci a coupé
le bout de son doigt.

à jouer dehors avec ses amies. Elles s'amusaient à grimper dans un arbre en face de la maison de l'une d'elles. Cindy a grimpé jusqu'en haut de l'arbre et s'est assise sur la branche. La branche qu'elle tenait a cassé et elle a atterri sur le dos. Encore une fois ses amies l'ont emmené à la maison et elle a dû aller à l'hôpital pour un examen. Aucune fracture mais elle s'était tout de même fait mal au bras.

Cindy a eu plusieurs accidents; je suis surprise qu'elle ait puisse rendre jusqu'à 41 ans. Je veux dire, elle s'est fait frapper par une voiture, a perdu un bout de doigt, et a perdu connaissance quelques fois. Cindy est ma mère et si elle n'était pas là en ce moment, je n'existerais pas! Elle aurait pu être très blessée. C'est pourquoi chaque fois que je traverse la rue, je regarde de chaque côté et si une voiture s'en vient, j'attends qu'elle passe.

Language: French
Translated by: ???

My Future Job

My future will probably be filled with animals. Do you want to know why?

I would like to be a veterinarian because I like animals like cats, dogs, birds, hamsters, bunnies, fish, and ferrets. I like cats because they are cute, fluffy, and self-cleaning. Dogs are cool because they can be cuddly and fun to play with. Hamsters are very small and sometimes funny and birds are cool because they fly and have beautiful wings.

A couple of days ago at school, I helped a little bird that got attacked by a cat and had an eye frozen shut. I felt sorry for the little thing.

I like to help animals so other people can have pets to play with if they're bored and lonely. There's only one problem, if I want to be a veterinarian, I will have to take science classes to gain the knowledge to take care of animals.

Telling you this brings back lots of good memories for me; memories with cats, dogs, hamsters, fish, and lots of other animals I had before. So, now you know why I would like to be a veterinarian. I hope you make a very good choice with your future job!

Amie Ladouceur, Grade 4 Student

Ma future va etre probablement plein d'animaux. Est-ce que tu sait pourquoi?

Je veux un vétérinaire par ce que j'aime les animaux comme des chats, des chiens, des oiseaux, des hamsters, des lapins, des poissons, et des furets. J'aime des chats par ce que ils sont mignons, doux, et ils sont propre. Des chiens sont cool par ce que ils peut etre câliner et   . Des hamsters sont tres petit et parfois drôle et des oiseaux sont cool par ce que ils volent et ils ont des ailes coloré.

Quelque jour avant à mon école, j'ai aidé un petit oiseau qui était attaqué par un chat et a eu une œil gelée. J'était désolé pour le petit oiseau.

J'aime aider des animaux pour que les autres personnes peut avoir des animaux. Il y a juste un problème, si je voudrais etre un vétérine, je dois apprend le science pour savoir comment guérir les animaux.

Quand je raconte ça, ça me done beaucoup de memoir pour moi. Des memoires avec des chats, chiens, hamsters poisson, et beaucoup d'animaux j'ai eu avant. Alors, maintenant tu sais pourquoi je veut etre un vétérinaire. J'espere que tu fait un bon decision avec ton emploi future

Language: French
Translated by: Mireille Comte, French Teacher

My Hockey Career

When I was eight years old I decided I was going to be a great hockey player. I had friends who were great hockey players. So, I figured I could be a great hockey player too. They played on Saturday mornings in the winter, and I heard all about it on Monday mornings at school.

The only problem I had was that my family owned the bowling alley and Saturday morning was when all the kids bowled in a bowling league. I had always bowled on Saturday morning and I think it was expected that I would always bowl on Saturday morning.

When I talked to my parents they said it would be okay, but I knew they were surprised. I had two older brothers and one younger brother and we had all bowled on Saturday mornings. When your parents own the bowling alley that's what you do, you bowl. I also knew that it would be an inconvenience for my parents. They would have to drive me to the rink, help me with my hockey equipment, and then drive me home after the games. I guess I was too young to think about that.

However, I did play and I wasn't very good. I quickly realized that I wasn't as good at skating as my friends. They had been skating for longer then me. I was slow and always a little behind the other boys. I also realized I wasn't as good at controlling the puck or making passes. I didn't get very many shots on net. On Monday mornings the boys would talk about the great plays they made and the goals they scored. I hadn't scored a goal or made any great plays. I was getting discouraged.

My mother kept driving me to the rink every Saturday morning. My parents never asked me to stop playing hockey. They never said I was better at bowling, and should go back to bowling.

As the last game was approaching my dad bought me a new stick and wrapped it with green duct tape. No one else on the team had a stick with green duct tape.

During the game there was a pile up in front of the other team's net. Several players on both teams had fallen down. There were sticks on the ice and the puck was somewhere in the middle of the pile. Suddenly the goal light went on and the referee shouted, "Goal". Our team cheered and everyone was excited. Then we wondered who scored the goal. The referee said the goal was scored by the "green stick". I was given the goal, my first goal.

On Monday morning I got to brag about that goal. I never scored another goal that year, and never played organized hockey after that one season. I went back to bowling. I was good at that. However, I remember that year and how my parents supported me. My hockey career may have been short but I sure remember that green stick.

Randy Little, Vice Principal

Ma carrière de hockey

Quand j'étais neuf ans j'ai décidé que je serais un joueur de hockey extraordinaire. J'avais des amis qui étaient des joueurs de hockey extraordinaires. Alors, j'ai figuré que moi aussi je pouvais être autant extraordinaire qu'eux. Ils jouaient tous les samedi matins en hiver, et je devrais entendre toutes les histoires les lundi matins à l'école.

Le seul problème que j'avais, était que mes parents possédaient le boulodrome, et samedi matin c'était quand tous les enfants jouaient dans une ligue. J'avais toujours joué aux quilles sur les samedi matins. Quand vos parents possèdent le boulodrome c'est qu'est ce que vous faites, vous jouer aux quilles. Je savais aussi que ça serait un inconvénient pour mes parents. Ils devraient me conduire à l'arène, m'aider avec mon équipement, puis me conduire à la maison après les jeux. Je suppose que j'étais trop jeune de penser à ces choses.

Cependant, j'ai joué et je n'étais pas très bon. J'ai rapidement réalise que je n'était pas autant bon au patinage que mes amis. Ils avaient beaucoup plus d'expérience que moi. J'étais lent, et toujours un peu en arrière des autres garçons. J'ai réalise que je n'était pas bon a contrôler la rondelle ou a passer la rondelle. Je n'ai pas réussi beaucoup d'essaies sur le filet. Chaque lundi les garçons dans mon classe parlaient de toutes leurs magnifiques essaies et de tous les buts qu'ils ont réussi. Je n'avait pas encore réussi un but, et j'ai commence à être un peu découragé.

Ma mère à continue à me conduire a l'arène tous les samedi matins. Mes parents ne m'ont jamais demandé d'arrêter à jouer au hockey. Ils ne m'ont jamais dit que j'étais plus bon aux quilles et que je devrais retourner à cela.

Quand le dernier jeu approchait, mon père m'a acheté un nouveau bâton et il l'a couvert en 'bande' vert. Personnes d'autre sur l'équipe avait un bâton couvert de ruban vert.

Durant le dernier jeu il y avait un beaucoup de personnes devant le filet de l'autre équipe. Plusieurs joueurs sont tombés. Il y avait plusieurs bâtons sur la glace, et la rondelle était quelque part dans le milieu. Soudainement, la lumière de but est allumée et l'arbitre a crié « But ! ». Notre équipe était très excitée. Mais personne ne savait qui a réussi le but. L'arbitre a dit que le but était réussi par le « bâton vert ». J'ai réussi le but, mon premier but.

Le lundi matin je pouvais parler de mon but avec tout le monde. Je ne suis jamais réussi un autre but cette année là, et je n'ai jamais joue dans une ligue après cette année. J'ai retourné à jouer aux quilles. J'était bon à cela. Cependant, je me souviens de cette année et comment mes parents étaient très de support. Ma carrière de hockey était courte, mais je me souviens bien du bâton vert.

Language : French
Translated by : ???

Where's my bike?

Ow! Memories can hurt! I was biking along the sidewalk near the Quickie, when I noticed the light was green, so I did not slow down. Unfortunately for me, my bike, and everyone who became involved, the light turned yellow and a car making a turn "couldn't see me". Obvious outcome: the car hit me. Not so obvious, I flew onto and off the hood of said car and into the front of a very angry looking bus.

I was quite dazed (KO'd). The bus driven waves me to sit down. In the ambulance my first question was: "Where's my bike?" Fortunately, I was not really hurt, except for bruises all over my body. Now whenever I ride my bike, I ask myself....... Where's my helmet?

Zachary Johnson, Grade 8 Student

Où est ma bicyclette

Je me promenais en bicyclette sur le trottoir près du dépanneur quand j'ai vu que le feu de circulation était vert alors je n'ai pas ralenti pour traverser la rue. Malheureusement pour moi, le feu est soudainement devenu jaune et un conducteur d'auto ne pouvait pas me voir et il n'a pas ralenti. Alors l'auto m'a frappé…Boum! Je me suis retrouvé sur le capot de la voiture et éventuellement devant un autobus de ville. J'étais très abasourdi! Le conducteur d'autobus m'a dit de m'asseoir. La première question que j'ai posé à l'ambulancier était 'Où est ma bicyclette?' Heureusement, je n'était pas gravement blessé sauf pour des bleus ici et la. Maintenant quand je fais de la bicyclette je me pose toujours la question : 'Où est mon casque?'

Language : French
Translated by : Richard Smith, French Teacher

My Family

I have a brother, Bruce, and a sister, Garmai. I like Bruce to read to me and draw pictures for me. I like to play tag with Garmai and Bruce. I also love playing with my Teddy. I help my Mom and Dad clean the house and cook. I really like to eat chicken and rice and spaghetti and salad. My family is wonderful. I love them a lot.

Paul Mulbah, Kindergarten Student

Ma Famille

J'ai un frère Bruce et un soeur Garmai. J'aime quand il me lit une histoire et quand il dessine des images aussi. J'aime jouer au chat perché avec Garmai et Bruce. J'aime aussi jouer avec mes oursons. J'aide a mes parents à nettoyer la maison et à cuisiner. J'adore manger le poulet, le riz, le spaghetti et les salades. Ma famille est formidable. Je les aime beaucoup.

Language : French
Translated by : Richard Smith, French Teacher

Trip to Shawville

My favourite family memory is when my brother Garrett, my dad, Ashley and I go to Shawville. We go to Shawville to visit my dad and grandparents. We go on our trip every second weekend. When we get to Shawville we play games and eat some french fries and chicken fingers or fish sticks. I like to read with my grandparents and finish my homework with them. We pack up again and then we go to school. I like going to Shawville. It is fun!

Quentin Young, Grade 2 Student

Voyage à Shawville.

Mon souvenir de famille préféré est quand mon frère Garrett, mon père, Ashley et moi allons à Shawville. Nous allons à Shawville visiter mon père et mes grands-parents. Nous faisons notre visite à tous les deux semaines. Quand nous arrivons à Shawville nous jouons à des jeux et nous mangeons des pommes frittes, et des bâtonnets de poulet ou de poisson. J'aime lire avec mes grands-parents et terminer mes devoirs avec eux. Nous plions bagage et ensuite nous allons à l'école. J'aime aller à Shawville. C'est très amusant !

Language: French
Translated by: ???

Mineral Rock Collection from Italy

On June 30 2002, my son Pascal and I left the country for France. This voyage was a gift for Pascal. He had been studying so hard, and all in English, in order to earn himself two scholarships to help pursue his studies at university. He did succeed. My wish was to reward him.

Once in France, Pascal and I visited the region called Provence, Nice and the little country of Monaco. With the car, we then took the ferryboat to Bastia, in Corsica.

Corsica is part of France and is located on the eastern side of France, in the Mediterranien Sea. In Europe, it is often referred to as the island of Beauty. The ocean was very agitated and we both felt sea sick. Once on the island, we visited the city of Adjaccio and the house where Napoleon Bonaparte was born. Along the road, we could see cows and pigs.

In Solenzara, the little village where we stayed for ten days, we met a journalist from Quebec. He told us to go on Elba island, where there was more to see on Napoleon. Thus, from Bastia, island of Corsica, to Portoferraio, Elba island, we took an other ferryboat. On the boat, there was a boutique. In the boutique, there was this beautiful mineral rock collection. The rock samples were all so pretty and all came from Elba island. We decided to purchase it as a souvenir. What a nice souvenir indeed!

Here are the names, in Italian, of the rock samples there are in the collection: serpentino, diaspro, calcite, aventurine, aragonite, limonite, ilvaite, crisocolla, granati, sodalite, gesso, magnetite, ocra, amianto, granito, fosforite, epidoto, opale.

Back on the continent, we went in the Alpes. In Chamonix, at the foot of the Mont Blanc, there was a nice museum with all the different rocks that can be found in the mountains. It was simply fascinating.

What a great trip this has been for Pascal and I!

Mireille Comte, French Teacher

Collection de Pierres d'Italie

Le 30 juin de l'an 2002, mon fils Pascal et moi sommes partis pour la France. Ce voyage était un cadeau pour Pascal. Il avait travaillé fort à l'école, en étudiant en anglais, afin d'obtenir deux bourses d'études pour l'université. Il avait réussi. Je voulais le récompenser.

Une fois en France, Pascal et moi avons visité la Provence, Nice et le petit pays de Monaco. Avec la voiture, nous avons pris le traversier jusqu'à Bastia, en Corse. La Corse est une île située à l'est de la France, dans la mer Méditerranée. Elle fait partie de la France. En Europe, on l'appelle l'île de beauté. L'océan était très agité. Pascal et moi avons eu le mal de mer. Arrivés en Corse, nous avons visité la ville et la maison natale de Napoléon Bonaparte : Ajaccio. C'était magnifique et très intéressant. Le long de la route, on pouvait voir des vaches et des cochons.

Arrivés à Solenzara, petit village où nous sommes restés pendant dix jours, nous avons rencontré un journaliste du Québec. Il nous a dit de visiter l'île d'Elbe, en Italie. Là, il y avait beaucoup à voir sur Napoléon. Alors, depuis Bastia, île de Corse jusqu'à Portoferraio, île d'Elbe, Pascal et moi avons pris un autre traversier. Sur le bateau, il y avait une boutique. Dans la boutique, il y avait cette belle collection de roches minérales, toutes aussi jolies les unes que les autres et toutes de l'île d'Elbe. On a décidé d'acheter la collection. Un souvenir, un beau souvenir.

Voici les différentes roches de la collection. Les noms sont en italien : serpentino, diaspro, calcite, pirite, ematite, quarzo, ametista, aventurina, aragonite, limonite, ilvaite, crisocolla, granati, sodalite, gesso, magnetite, ocra, amianto, granito, fosforite, epidoto, opale.

De retour sur le continent, nous sommes allés dans les Alpes. Puis, à Chamonix, au pied du Mont Blanc, nous avons visité un très beau musée où il y avait aussi toute une collection des roches que l'on trouve dans les montagnes. C'était tout simplement fascinant.

Quel beau voyage nous avons fait, Pascal et moi !

Language: French
Translated by: Mireille Comte, French Teacher

Hawthorne *Writes*
because everyone has a story...

YOUR FUTURE IS NOW

2. Albanian – Shqip

Albanian is spoken by an estimated 3 million people around the world. Albanian is spoken mostly in Albania, however, it can also be found in Greece, Turkey and Ukraine.

Hello Canada

My family and I came from Kosovo, which is the country I was born in. It was the craziest adventure of my life. The reason why we moved to Canada is because there was a war going on in Kosovo. So when we arrived in Canada, no one in my familyn knew how to speak English and it was very hard for us. When we moved into a house, we waited a few days so that we could sign up for a school. The next day, my mom and dad has signed me, John and Shawn at a school called Carson Grove. When it was time for us to go to school, it was difficult for me, John, and Shawn to understand the teachers. We learned a little English in a couple of days. We only went to that school for about one year or perhaps less because where we use to live, we didn't have any neighbours. All we had was only our big house and the rest was cornfields, so my parents, Ahmed and Fatuma, decided we needed more neighbours to help us learn English. After two weeks, we had moved to Russell Road.

Our home on Russell Road was better. There were lots of kids playing outside. Around two days later, I and my brothers had made some friends. They were so nice to us. We all went to play at the basketball court because there was one free. So we played until 5 in the evening. The next day, my mom and sister had signed up for English and my little sister had signed up for children's daycare. It took them about two weeks to learn enough English to be understood.

Well, I guess my family's adventure had been very hard, but I think it was well worth the efforts.

Mevlide Ahmeti, Grade 5 Student

Familya ime dhe une vfimi pee kosover, si është
ku jam lindër. Është kënden une shume vend.
Sepre na kina largnar Ni kanad është se është
kënd një luftë ne kosov. kur kina orri ne kanad
familja ime nuk ka dit gish me fol englisht
edhe u kendën shum zër per mu. kur e kina bli një
shtepi kina prit pagës për me nënshkruar per shkoll.
Seterën did Nana dhe Babi Nënshkruar mu, John, dhe
shawn për shkoll Carson Grove. Kur u këndër gjoha
per me shkrvar në shkoll u kënd shum zur per mu
John dhe shawn me dit shka Tu Mundimën mësuisia.
kina mesu Englishi mas pak dif. Na kina shkuar te
shkolla. Sill për një vjet sepre shtëpi ësh kendër larg pre shkolles
Fill kina pas një wen ne shume shtalbën tani Mami dhe
Babi tha ina tu largoias te Russell.

   Shtëpia ne Russell është kendën ma e mir. Shume foi
to lugtër për jasht. Mas dy did une dhe vlau im kina ben shum
shokë. kina shkuar me lujte top kto nju iterder fol. kina
lujtër deri pas. Djitën tyetër motra ka pën shkuar për Englishell
dhe motra e vogël pre ojerzi ne kshir. kva oloshtor z jau
ne did ne fol mir englishet ne gramatis. Po shume vend
kina shkuar pr shua sene kina bener.

Language: Albanian
Translated by: Veli Selmani, Grade 7 Student

Coming to Canada

When our airplane landed in Trenton Ontario from Kosova we were met by
a couple named Hugo and Agnes. We lived with them for two years. They helped my family learn how to speak English and adjust to our new country. When I started school Hugo and Agnes came with us to help our parents understand. When Hugo and Agnes came to my house they would come downstairs to see my budgie birds. There are seven birds now the parents and five babies. Hugo and Agnes helped my family a lot. They would take us on trips and go biking. Last year it was sad for us because Hugo passed away from cancer but we still visit with Agnes. I will never forget Hugo and how he helped out family.

Durim Ahmeti, Grade 7 Student

Tu Ardhes Në Canad

Kur airaplani u mlidh tok Ne Trenton pre kosovës
dë na kun fall si e kan pas emësin Hugo and
Agnes. Na kinq banu me ata per dij vjet.
Na kan nimuar qish ne fol eylisht dhe
shu me ban ne Canod. Kur ja kum nis
shkollen Hugo dhe Agnis na ka nimuar, Kur
Huga dhe Agnes nrcin te shtëpia in
vjen në podimm dhe mi kshir vreeygete
Hugo dhe Agnes Nenon famiën shum. Na morrin
me biciklota mi ngra. Vjet goter nuk u këhdën
mir nepce Hugo ka diki. po hula e
visitojm Agnes. Kurr nuk e harroj Hugn çish
na ka nimuar familën

Language: **Albanian**
Translated by: Veli Selmani, Grade 7 Student

Hawthorne *Writes*
because everyone has a story...

3. Amharic – አማርኛ

Amharic is spoken by an estimated 17 million people in Ethiopia. Other languages spoken in Ethiopia include Oromo, Tigrinya, Arabic and English. Amharic can also be found spoken in parts of Egypt, Israel and Sweden.

My Family

There are 6 people in my family. Their names are Mom, Dad, me, Linda, Hayat and Fuwad. I love my family very much because my Mom and Dad hug me. I love my brother because I love him. I love Hyatt too much!

Rihanna Omar, Kindergarten Student

ሃኛ ፡ ቤተሰብ ፡ ውስጥ ፡ ስቃስት ፡ ሰዎኝ ፡
ኢኮ ፡ ይሄነሱ ግ ፡ ስጧ ፡ ሃነፀ ፡ እገፀ ፡
ሃዬ ፡ ኢንፃ ፡ ሃያት ፡ ሃነ ፡ ቀእዴ ፡
ገኘ ፡፡

ሃዬ ፡ ቤተስቤን ፡ በጧግ ፡ ሃስወዳ ከሆ ፡ ግ
ኢነያተግ ፡ ሃነፀ ፡ ሃነ ፡ እገፀ ፡ ሃኢነን
ያቅናቅስ ፡ ወንዱግኘን ፡ ሃስወዳ ቀከሆ ፡
ግ ኢነያተግ ፡ ሃስወዳ ቀከሆ ፡ ሃነ ፡
ሃያትን ፡ በጧግ ፡ ሃስወዳ ተከሆ ፡፡

ፈዬፈ

Language: Amarhic
Translated by: Ahmed Omar

The Luckiest Day of My Life

In February, I won two jars of candy. One of the jars was filled with hot cinnamon hearts and the other was filled with jellybeans. The jar with hot cinnamon hearts had 1963 and the jar of jellybeans had 386. I was really happy when I saw the large pink construction paper at the door saying that I had won!

There were three jars of candy and the person who won the other jar was Jane. She is a girl with brown hair. She won these reddish-pinkish marshmallows.One marshmallow looked like it weighed five grams! I thought the marshmallow would taste chewy and hard at the same time.

I was really glad I won the jellybean jar because that was the jar I wanted to have. The colours of the jellybeans were green, white, and red. I'm not really sure why I didn't like the red jellybeans. I thought they were really bad.

I was surprised when I won both of the jars. That day was the luckiest day of my life! I kept jumping up and down. My sister wanted the jar that had the 1963 hot cinnamon hearts. I ended up sharing both of the jars of candy with sixteen people. Also, on that day, someone in my class had a birthday so my teacher brought in a box of 20 timbits. I was really full after eating the candy and three timbits!

Linda Omar, Grade 4 Student

በቅ·ሰነት·ወር·ሙሴ·ሁሴን·ሞሳወሕ·ኅባበ
ሕ·ሙሴኝበዛሁሁ·ኅዝዓሰ·ሞሳወሕ·ወሰሕ·
የወዝ·ፋያኝ·ቀሬፋ·ዓበቃሕ·ጎርዕ·ሙሕ·ሕ
ሕዝወ·ሞሳወሕ·ዓዎዎ·ወሕ·ደበቃሕ·ጎርዕ
ኝሁወ·1963·ሙሕኔ·የወዝ·ትርሁወ·ቀሬፋ·የሞ
ጎርዕ·ነሬ·ዓዓሕ·ሞሳወሕ·ወሕኝ·ዴ౬ዝ·
የበቃሕ·ጎርዕ·ኅበዓሕ·ሞሳወሕ·ወሕ·ዝዳ౬
ሕዝ·ጀየተሰኝወዬ·ዓሕትዝ·ኅነርዝጎኝበዝዓጎዝ·ዓሕ·
ዝዓዬ·ዮዓርዓዓ·ዬዓሎዝ౬ሕ·ዝሕ·ዮዓዓ
ሰዓቀ·ሕፋ·ዝዝኝሰሕጎ౬ሳ·የወ ዝ౬ጎዕ·ዓዓሸ·
ሰዓዝ·ሕፋ·ትሕዝ౬·ሕፋ·ዓዎዎ·ዓሕትዝ·ኅነርዝ
ዓዓ·ዝዝ౬·ሕዓዝ·ሞሳወሕ·ቀ౬ዓዓሕ·ኅዓር·ሕሕዓ౬
ዝ·ሞሳወሕ·ኅበዓሕ·የዓ౬ዝ౬ፋወ·ኝ౬·ኅዓር
ሕሕዓዎ·ዓዓዓ·ፀ౬ር·ዝሕዝ·ሕ౬·ኝዝ··
ሕሕዓዎ·የ౬ዝ౬ፋፒወ·ቀዝ·ሕዝኔ·ርዝዝ·
ዓሸዓዝሕዝ·ኅዓር·ሕዝዝዝ·ዓዖ·ዎዎሕዝ
ዝዝሕትዝ·ኝዓዓዝዝ·ዓዬዓ·ዝወ·ሕሕዝዓዓ
ሕዓዎ·ዓሸዓዝሕዝ·የዎዛወ·ዝዓዓዎዛዛ
·ሕዝኔ·ዓዝዝሰ·ቀወዓሕዝዶ႟··
ሕዝዝዓዎ·ዝዓዎ·ዓሕትዝ·ኝዓርዝ·ዓሸዝ
ዖዝዝ·የዓቃሕ·ጎርዕ·ኅዓዛሕ·ሞሳወ
ሕ·ዓዓዝኔዝዝዓዎ·ዝዝ·ሞሳወሕ·ኝዓር·
የዝዝዓዓዝ·የዓቃሕ·ጎርዕ·ኅዓዛሕ·
ዝሕ౬ዓዎ··ኅዓዝ౬ዓዝ౬·ዝ౬ዎዎ·ሕዝኔ

ቀና፡ ነበር፡ በመግቶም፡ ሠላምም፡
ቀቀን፡ የበቴክ፡ ገርጀ፡ ኅብረትክ፡
ካበመ ዓመተ ጊዜ ገብቶም፡ በሃሰበም፡ በጠም፡
መሻሼ፡ መስከረ፡ ታየኝ፡፡
ሠላም፡ በጠም፡ ተገሪምነት፡ ሀከተን
ም፡ ጠርመለየ፡ በማሸገኮ፡ ደን፡ ቀን፡
በዜመቴ፡ መሰሳ፡ ሠካኬ፡ ተን፡ ነበር፡
ሠላም፡ በከመገ ቀርኖ፡ ሠከቀ፡ ሠና፡ ሠና
ፍ፡ ሠደበበ፡ ዘከበግብት፡ ሠወሀቴም፡
ገከ፡ 1963 ኅብረትክ፡ ጠርመለቼ፡ ልበገ
ነበር፡ ሠላም፡ በመመደረሸ፡ ከካሳቤት
ዴሳት፡ ሰዎች፡ ጋር፡ በመሆን፡ ሀከቶን
ም፡ ጠርመለስ፡ ኅብረትክ፡ ተከበሮበት፡
ካንጋሀምም፡ በዛን፡ ቀን፡ በአገልጋዮቹ፡
መሰሳ፡ የኢንተር ሆቴ፡ በኋላ፡ ነበር፡
ከስተማሪዎችን፡ ሃይ፡ ትንበት፡ መክ.
ካርቶን፡ ከምዕተ፡ ነበር፡ ሠላም፡ በጠ
ም፡ ጠማበ፡ ነበር፡ ሂሳብ፡ ትንበት፡ ሣር፡
የተከደፈን፡ ኅብረትክ፡ ከከሆኑ በሆኑ፡፡

ከንጎ፡ ሁጨመሬ

Language: Amharic
Translated by: Ahmed Omar

Hawthorne *Writes*
because everyone has a story...

4. Arabic – العربية

Arabic is the first language spoken by an estimated 206 million people around the world. It is thought that are 246 million people who speak Arabic as a second language. Arabic is spoken across the Middle East, North Africa and in other Muslim countries around the world.

The Childhood of My Mother

You might think you know everything about your family, but really there are many things hidden under the rug. Oral history helps you discover things about people close to you in your life. People who you care about a lot and people who equally care very much for you.

Nowadays, there is much diversity in the world. This new emerging diversity encourages many people to talk more freely and share their experiences about their homeland. The sharing of stories and the diversity of cultures allows the world to learn more about other people and to understand and celebrate our differences.

It doesn't matter where you come from, it's whom you are inside and no one should be shy to share their story. Everybody should feel confident to talk about their childhood, life or anything different or diverse about themselves. That is why I interviewed my mother, Mrs. Anisa Metwally, to learn more about how she lived when she was my age and to allow her to share her story with every single one of you out there.

I was born and raised in Alexandria, Egypt near the Mediterranean Sea, where the air smelled fresh and clean. The dolphins jumped up and down splashing in the water creating live waves. The dolphins sang beautiful dolphin songs welcoming spring, and exiting winter. The water was clean and fresh and sparkled in the sun.

I was the youngest of six siblings, two sisters, and four brothers. We lived in a huge house that sat in front of the sparkling sea. I have very fond memories of my childhood. I used to sit and watch dolphins jumping in the sea, and I would spend hours sitting relaxed in front of the water, while writing poetry. It was my favourite thing to do as a child.

My other hobbies were reading books, writing poetry and stories. Although I had a gigantic house that had every thing that interested me, I didn't have a TV. I only had a simple radio, but it was full of wonders, and when I listened to it I drew pictures in my head of what I was hearing using my amazing imagination.

I had to walk to school because there were no school buses. The teachers were extremely strict, and anyone who made any mistakes faced harsh consequences. However, I was a serious student who respected my peers and teachers. I also used to sing at school concerts. I in particular remember singing every year on Mother's Day, because I really loved my beautiful, caring mother, and I sang from my heart.

In 1967, when I was 10 years old, two terrible things happened in my life. First, in the winter of 1967 my grandfather died and we all suffered a great loss because he was very kind and we all truly loved him. My mother fell ill from the awful death of her father and she stayed in bed for months. Following this in June 1967, a cruel war started in Egypt. I woke up everyday frightened from the warning bells and airplanes flying over our house.

My family had to move to the other side of the city, for two reasons. Firstly there was a war going on, and secondly our beautiful house was unfortunately going to collapse because it was getting old.

The new house was smaller and I didn't have many neighbours or friends because it was a wide-open, deserted place. After the war, we suffered from an economic disaster in Egypt, but because I was determined I went to a new school, made new friends, and kept my positive attitude towards life.

Although I tried my best to overcome everything, there were some things that I still didn't like. As our house was far from many places, I sometimes had to walk in the rain a great distance and I when I arrived home I would be soaking wet. There was however some things that improved. Although the financial status in my family increased, our house was too small for a big family like mine. My siblings and I all shared one room. This was really difficult, but we all had to go through this experience to lead us to a more successful life.

Though it was unfortunate that all my family had to suffer, we survived many harsh things and we all grew up to have a great and successful life. As a result of all these things we lived through when we were young, we grew up to be supportive parents.

Interviewee: Anisa Metwally
Interviewer: Ebtsam Metwally

Ebtsam Metwally, Grade 7 Student

طفولة امي

ربما تعتقد انك تعلم كل شيء عن عائلتك ولكن في الواقع هناك اشياء كثيرة لاتعلمها. القصص العائلية تساعدك باكتشاف اشياء كثيرة عن الاشخاص المقربين اليك , اشخاص تهتم بهم كثيرا وهم بدورهم يهتمون بك .

في الوقت الراهن هناك اختلافات كبيرة بين الناس حول العالم وهذه الاختلافات تشجع اناس كثيرين للتكلم بحرية ومشاركة الاخرين خبراتهم وذكرياتهم عن الوطن الاصلي , ان تبادل القصص مع اختلاف العادات والتقاليديسمح بالتعلم بصورة واسعة عن بعضهم البعض وتفهم اوجه اختلافاتهم.

لايهم من اين اتيت , ولكن المهم من انت من الداخل ولايجوز ان يخجل احد من طرح قصته على الاخرين . لابد ان يشعر الجميع بالثقة والتكلم عن طفولتهم أو أشياء اخرى تميزهم عن الاخرين . لذلك اجريت حوارا مع امي السيدة انيسه متولي كي اتعلم اكثر كيف كانت تعيش وهي في مثل عمري وان تسمح لي بمشاركة قصتها مع الجميع.

قالت: لقد ولدت وتربيت في الاسكندرية وهي مدينة ساحلية على شاطيء البحر الابيض المتوسط حيث الهواء المنعش المشبع برائحة البحر . كنت اشاهد الدلافين وهي تقفز في الماء وتنشر الرزاز مكونة موجات حية من الماء والدلافين , وكانت الدلافين تغني باصوات جيلة مودعة الشتاء ومرحبة بالربيع القادم وكان ماء البحر ان ذاك نظيف ويلمع تحت اشعة الشمس .

لقد كنت الاصغر لسبعة اخوة ولي اختان واربعة اخوان كنا نعيش في بيت كبير على شاطيء البحر البراق , ولقد اعتدت ان اجلس بالساعات لاشاهد الدلافين وهي تقفز في ماء البحر وامضي اوقت في كتابة القصص والشعر وهي كانت هوايتي المفضلة, ولقد كانت لدي هوايات اخرى بجانب القراءة والكتابة , ولقد كان في هذا الوقت لايوجد تلفاز في مصر ولكن كان لدي جهاز المذياع المليء بالبرامج الممتعة لي والذي كنت استمع اليه وارسم صورا في خيالي لكل مااسمعه فلقد كنت استخدم خيالي الواسع للاستمتاع بما اسمع .

لقد كنت اذهب الي المدرسة سيرا على الاقدام لانه لم يكن هناك حافلات للمدرسة , وكانت المدرسات حازمات واي خطأ يصدر من التلاميذ يقابل بعقاب رادع لم اذق طعمه لاني كنت تلميذة مجتهدة ومحبوبة وكنت احترم زملائي ومعلماتي .

لقد كنت اغني في حفلات المدرسة وبالتحديد كنت اغني في حفلة عيد الام من كل عام حبا في امي الجميلة الطيبة كثيرا ولذلك كان غنائي لها من اعماق قلبي .

وحينما بلغت العاشرة من عمري وبالتحديد عام 1967 حدث امرين خطيرين في حياتي ففي شتاء 1967 مات جدي لامي ولقد تأثرنا جميعا لفراقه لانه كان طيبا وكنا جميعا متعلقين به ونحبه كثيرا ولقد مرضت امي مرضا شديدا حزنا عليه ومكثت شهور في فراش المرض وفي نفس العام وبالتحديد خلال شهر يونيو حدثت حرب بين مصر واسرائيل وكانت حربا شديدة ومرعبة , فلقد اعتدت الاستيقاظ على اصوات صافرات الانذار والطائرات تحلق فوق بيتنا .

واضطرت عائلتي ان تنتقل الي الجهة الاخرى من المدينة لسببين , الاول كان بسبب الحرب والثاني لان بيتنا اصبح عتيقا ومعرضا للانهيار .

انتقلنا الى البيت الجديد الذي لم يكن واسعا ولم يكن لدينا جيران أو اصدقاء لان المنطقة كانت حديثة وصحراوية .
بعد الحرب مرت مصر بازمة اقتصادية ولكن كنت لدي اصرار وعزيمة قوية لتخطي الصعاب فذهبت الى مدرسة جديدة وسرعان ماأصبح لي اصدقاء جدد واحتفظت بشخصيتي القوية الايجابية تجاه الحياة .
وبذلت اقصى مافي جهدي لتخطي كل الازمات ولقد كانت هناك اشياء مازلت لاحبها مثل ان بيتنا كان بعيدا عن كل شيء حتى انه في بعض الاحيان كان لابد ان اسير تحت المطر مسافات طويلة و كنت اصل الى البيت وملابسي مبللة من المطر , فضلا عن الظروف الصعبة فلقد كنت انا واخوتي البنات نشترك في غرفة نوم واحدة , ولقد كان ذلك صعبا ولكن لم تستمر المعاناة طويلا وتحسنت الظروف المادية لعائلتي شيئا فشيء وتخطينا جميعا التجربة التي قادتنا الى حياة ناجحة فيما بعد

ورغم كل المعاناة التي مررنا بها في حياتنا تخطينا الصعوبات وكبرنا جميعا ونجحنا في حياتنا ونتيجة لكل هذه الاشياء الذي مررنا بها ونحن صغار فحينما كبرنا اصبحنا اباء وامهات اقوياء ندعم اطفالنا ونهتم بهم .

الضيفة: انيسه متولي
المحاورة : ابتسام متولي

Language: Arabic
Translated by: Anisa Metwally, International Language Teacher

The Bear

My treasure is a bear. My treasure looks like a cute baby bear that can sing. The colour of the bear is brown. I got my treasure as a gift from my parents on Eid. It is important to me because I play with it a lot. Sometimes I take it to bed with me. It sings a beautiful, funny song. I can sing with it and dance too.

Reem Siage, Grade 1 Student

أَلدُب

كَنْزِي هو الدُبّ . كَنْزِي يَعني وكأنه الدُبّ الصغير .. لون الدُبّ بُنّي، لقد حصلتُ على كَنْزي كهديةٍ مقدمةٍ من أهلي بمناسبة العيد. وهو هديةٌ ثمينةٌ وهمّةٌ بالنسبة لي، لأنّي أُحبّه مَدّه كثيراً، وأحياناً أصطحبه لينامَ معي في سريري، وكذلك يعني أجمل الأغاني وأطرفها، وأنا أستطيع أن أغني معه وأرقص أيضاً.

ريم سياج

Language: Arabic
Translated by: Ghaji Siage

Treasure

My treasure is a photo album. It has a lot of pictures of my grandpa's pictures and my grandma's pictures, my mom really takes care of it, because it means a lot to her like I mean a lot to her. It even has pictures of her sisters and brothers because, my mom knew she was going to move away from Jordan to come to Canada, because my dad was living there and she wanted to live with him and my other step-brothers. So as I was saying my mom really takes care of it. When my mom is feeling sad and she's thinking about her family she would look back at the pictures and think of the stuff my grandpa and my grandma would do when she causes trouble. When my mom looks at those pictures, she would always sing a song, when she's looking at them I don't know why, it was probably a song my grandpa and my grandma used to sing. My mom took those pictures when she was like 23, it was in Jordon when she took them, since that day my grandpa died, and she kept the pictures of him then my dad came to Jordon and brought us here with our other brothers. My dad also has a treasure, it's a ring that my grandpa gave to him when he was going to die, and he told him to take of it. After 2 days my grandpa died and my dad had to take care of that ring. So every time my dad remembers my grandpa he would go in his room lock it and take out the ring, then he would stay in the room and think about all the stuff they used to do together, and how he took care of him. My grandpa gave my dad the ring before his dead by 2 days. He gave it to him when my dad was about 27 years old. He called my dad to my Grandpa's room and he told him since I am going to die soon I want you to have this ring, and I want you to take care of it. And every time u think about me, I want you to go in your room and think about me. So every time my dad and my mom felt sad about there family they would look back at there treasures.

Ahmad Al-Enzi, Grade 8 Student

الكنز

كنزي هو البوم صور فيه الكثير من
الصور لجدي وجدتي تعتني به أمي
كثيراً لأنه يعني الكثير لها ولي. يحتوي
هذا الألبوم على صور لأخواتها وأخوانها
فسوف ترحل عائلتي من الأردن إلى كندا
فعندما تشعر بحنين وإشتياق لهم.
تنظر إلى صورهم وتبدأ بغناء أغنية كان
يغنيها جدي وجدتي بإستمرار. التقطت
هذه الصور لأمي في الأردن عندما كان
عمرها ٣ عاماً ومنذ ذلك اليوم توفي
جدتي.

أبي أيضاً لديه كنز وهو خاتم أعطاه إياه
جدتي قبل أن يتوفى بيومين، وكان عمره ٧٥
عاماً واعتنى به والدي كثيراً ودائماً يقفل
أبي خبيرته ويتناول هذا الخاتم وينظر إليه
ويتذكر ما أوصاه به جدي بأن يهتم بهذا
الخاتم. لذا يشعر أمي وأبي بالحزن عندما
ينظرون إلى ذكرياتهم مع عائلاتهم.

Language: Arabic
Translated by: Anisa Metwally, International Language Teacher

My Traditions

In my Middle Eastern traditions women wear a scarf over their heads to cover their heads and neck. This scarf is called a hijab. The women wear the hijab so men don't see their hair. They only take the hijab in front of other women and their husband and kids. My mother and I like wearing hijabs because they look nice. I will be ready to wear a hijab when I am nine years old. I like to collect them because they are very pretty and come in different colours and styles. There are many different ways of wearing a hijab. Some people even wear pretty jewelry with the hijab. My mom uses shiny pins to keep the hijab in place. The pins come in different shapes like flowers or pretty bows. The women think the hijab looks very pretty on them. I also think I would look very nice if I wore a hijab. Almost all the women in my family wear a hijab and I look forward to wearing one myself.

Reem Moawiya, Grade 2 Student

عاداتنا وتقاليدنا

في ثقافتنا الإسلامية ترتدي النساء حجاباً تغطين شعرهنّ

وقد سمي حجاباً لأنه يحجب ستر المرأة عن أنظار الغرباء

ولكن تستطيع المرأة أن تخلع الحجاب أمام زوجها

وأولادها وأخوالها وأعمامها وأمام النساء الأخريات أثناء أي

في الحجاب أيضاً ونرى في الحجاب غطاءً جميلاً لستر الشعر

وقد بدأتُ أنا أحضّر نفسي لارتداء الحجاب عندما أصبحُ في

سن التاسعة. عندها سأشتري الكثير من الحجابات الجميلة

المختلفة الألوان. سوف أهتمّ باختيار الدبابيس المزركشة الملونة

والدبابسة مثل تلك التي ترتديها أمي. وترتم النساء المسلمات

أن يظهرن بشكل لائق. وحتى غيادات الوقت أنا المسلمة

أرتدي نفسي بصورة جميلة وأنيقة عندما سأرتدي الحجاب

Language: Arabic
Translated by: Ola Al Azak

My Family

There are nine people in my family. Their names are Mommy, Daddy, Faisal, Mohamed, Sheema, Sharef, Noura, Mariam and me, Sam.

I love my family because I get to go shopping with them and play with them as well. Something else I like about my family is that whenever I am sick they take care of me, and keep me warm. They help me meet new friends and keep me healthy and cheered me to go to school to learn. I love them because I get lots of new toys and get what I want from them. Another thing I like to do with them is to go out, play with them, and eat ice cream at the same time watch movies. I love my family and I know they love me too!

Sam Alharhara, Kindergarten Student

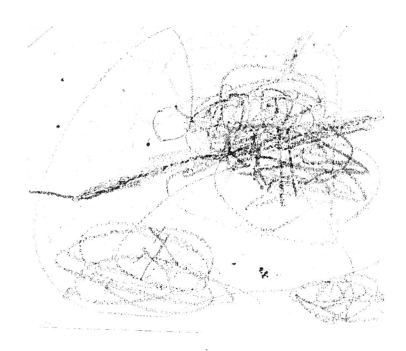

۞ سام وعائلته ۞

يوجد تسعة أشخاص في عائلتي وأسماءهم
أمي، أبي، فيصل، مريند، شيماء، شريف،
نوره، مريم، وأنا سام.

أنا أحب عائلتي لأنهم يأخذوني معهم للتسوق
و يلعبوا معي أيضاً. و أذكر أيضاً أن عائلتي
يواسوني عندما أكون مريضاً و يبقوني دائماً
و هم ساعدوني لكي ألتقي بأصحابي جدد
و يبقوني بصحة جيدة و يشجعوني لكي أذهب
للمدرسة لأتعلم. و أحب عائلتي لأني أحضر
منهم على كثير من الألعاب وكل ما أريده منهم.
وشيء آخر أحب أن نعمله معهم هو أن أخرج
في الخارج و ألعب معهم و نأكل الآيسكريم
في نفس الوقت الذي نتفرج فيه على الأفلام.
أنا أحب عائلتي و أنا أعرف أنهم يحبوني
أيضاً.

Language: Arabic
Translated by: ???

My Treasure

My treasure is a collection of sea shells. There are seven shells and one is large, three are medium, and three are small. They are shiny, beautiful, and beige, grey, brown colour. My mom got them from Port Sudan in the Red Sea. It reminds me about the sea and my family in Sudan. I like to listen to the sound in my ear. I imagine a snail inside the shells.

Rafa Abbas, Grade 1 Student

قصة الكنز

السلام عليكم ... سوف اقص عليكم قصة كنزي .
كنزي هو عبارة عن مجموعة من اصداف البحر .
هذا الكنز يحتوي على سبعة اصداف . تنقسم
الاصداف الى ثلاثة اصداف متوسطات وثلاثة اصداف
صغار وواحدة كبيرة . هذة الاصداف البحرية
جميلة و راقه و لم تخل مزيج من اللون البني
و الرمادي و البيج . لقد اهديت هذة الاصداف
البحرية من قبل تسودان . لير وتسودان هي مربيه
على البحر الاحمر . ما يميز بقية تحفة الاصدان
هو انها تذكرني بالبحر الاحمر و اسرتي في
قطر السودان . الفتأ احب ان استمع
الى الاصوات الصادرة من هذة الاصدان في اذني .
ايضأ اتخيل حيوات الحيوان وبقى داخل
هذة الاصدان عندما انظر داخلها .

Language: Arabic
Translated by: Abdelgadir Abbas

Disney

Have you ever had a wish come true? I did. The Wish Foundation gave me a wish to go somewhere and I picked Disney World.

On February 15, 2005 my family and I went to the airport in a limousine to fly to Disney World. On the airplane my brother and I ate chips and gum. We met a man at the airport who helped us rent a car and find where we would be living. A lady showed us the Ice Cream Palace and where other attractions were.

The first morning after we arrived we woke up got dressed and ate my breakfast. Other stuff than I went in our car to Disney World and went on the rides and other rides and I went to paint my face. My favorite rides were Spider Man and The Cat and The Hat and many more rides. We also went to Marine World and I saw dolphins and killer whales. I arrived back home and we went for a swim.

I was so happy there meeting new friends and having fun with my family. I wished it would never end. It was a wish come true.

Zeinab Borji, Grade 3 Student

رحلة إلى ديزني ورلد

في سنتي مرت ثانية طبطات بعايتة ـ لويشي قويا
لو جايتنا كانت على ديزني لاند انا واهلي
في ١٥ شباط ٥٠٠٠م ـ انا واهلي رحنا على الطار
بسيارة ليموزين حتى سافر إلى ديزني.
انا وضامي حطا اكلنا شبيبس وحلكم
لأنا رجل في الطار ناطرنا وساعدنا بكل شي
حتى جبنا سيارة ودورنا وبتي مانا نقعد في قبالا
وللمرآة لقد فرجتنا كل شي ووجود صونيك قعد
ايست كريم ولها سبيح وكل شي ووجود صونيك
ثاني يوم صبح فقنا ولبسنا وتوون قنا وجبنا
غراض تعلبنا ورحنا بالسيارة على ديزني ورد
وطلعنا بالاعاب وكل ماشينت وحوي ولونت وحين
اجمل لعبة كانت لعبتة سبيدرمان ولعبتة
طيارة ولعبة طاقية ولعاب كتير حلبايتو
كلمين رحنا على دلفين ورد وستريضت لفوف
ورجعنا على لبيت وتسبينا
وكنت كتير مبسوطة وستفدت عالم جديرة وابسطة
كتير وح عايلتي وبتمنا صدي الحقيقة ما تخلص
وترجع تسير حقيقة ـ

Language : Arabic
Translated by : Rodaina

Hawthorne *Writes*
because everyone has a story...

5. Bengali – বাংলা

Bengali is spoken by an estimated 211 million people around the world including people who learned it as a second language. Over 100 million people speak Bengali in Bangladesh. It is also spoken in India, Malawi, Nepal, to name a few countries.

My Family

I have one brother. His name is Nabil. He gives me piggyback rides. Sometimes when I am sad, Nabil can make me laugh. We like to play games like hide and seek.

I like to help my mom cook. I like to play tag with my dad. Our family likes to watch videos together.

I love my parents and my brother very much. My family is wonderful!

Naznin Ahmed, Kindergarten Student

আমার একটি ভাই আছে, তাহার নাম নাফিন, সে আমাকে
খেলিতে চায়, কিছু সময় হয়তো আমার ঙনি সমস্যা,
নাফিন আমাকে দিলে যাদির জিনিস তৈরি করে, আমরা
তাস খেলতে এবং সুলেমুরি খেলতে পছন্দ করি,

আমি আমার সাথে ব্যয় করতে চাহায়
করি, আমি আমার বাবার সাথে ব্যস্ত পানি খেলতে
পছন্দ করি, আমার পরিবার একসাথে ভিডিও
দেখতে পছন্দ করি,

আমি আমার বাবা / মা এবং আমার
ভাই কে খুব ভালোবাসি, আমার পরিবার সুখইসুখি

Language : Bengali
Translated by : ???

Hawthorne *Writes*
because everyone has a story...

YOUR FUTURE IS NOW

6. Chinese – 中文

It is estimated that there are over a billion people in the world who speak Chinese, making it the most commonly spoken language in the world. There are over 860 million people who speak Chinese as their first language in Mainland China. In addition, it is thought that as many as 178 million people learn Chinese as a second language.

Mandarin is known as Traditional Chinese. Cantonese is known as Simplified Chinese. Some words are not written the same way in both languages. The pronunciations of the words are very different, for example in the Mandarin language there are phonetic symbols and they are spoken in four different tones.

Language Description by: Colin Wu, Grade 8 Student

Something To Keep

I can close my eyes and still see my mom sitting at the old sewing machine and singing off-key. Her right foot would be moving the treadle and her hand would be guiding the material she was sewing. How she loved that old sewing machine!

The machine was an old Singer treadle sewing machine bought for my grandmother in 1920. It was a "state of the art" piece of equipment at that time. The sewing machine was shiny black and, when not in use, folded down into a beautiful oak sewing cabinet. The machine required no electricity and, just like a bike, worked on "foot power".

My Grandmother sewing clothes for 13 children on that machine and like the "Energizer Bunny", it just would not stop. When my grandmother died, the sewing machine was passed on to my mom who loved and cherished it. Although my mom did not make clothes for her children, she frequently used the machine to repair and mend items of clothing.

One year we decided to surprise my mom with a new electric sewing machine thinking we would make her life easier. She tried it a few times and then went right back to that old "foot machine".

When my mom died, my dad would not part with the sewing machine, but kept it in its place of honour in the corner in the living room. When he remarried, his new bride brought new furniture, including an electric sewing machine, with her. The old sewing machine was sent to a spot in the basement.

Each summer when I would visit my dad I would see the old machine looking older and older and each year I asked to take it back to Ottawa. One summer my dad surprised me by saying I could have it. When we got it back to Ottawa we realized how sad it really looked.

Over the summer, my husband had a meeting with an antique dealer who agreed to take the sewing machine and restore it. Just before

Christmas there was a knock at the door and to my delight a beautiful, restored sewing machine was brought into our home.

Each time I go into our dining room and look at this lovely, old sewing machine I am reminded of my grandmother and my mother. Our daughter, who lives in a one hundred and sixty year old house in Perth, tells me she has the perfect spot for this "treasure" when I leave it her.

Mary Dunne, Intermediate SELC Teacher

当我闭上我的眼睛，我看到了我的母亲坐在那台旧的缝纫机前，歌声伴随着她，她的右脚踩着缝纫机的踏板，她的手翻弄着布料，她是多么的喜欢这台旧缝纫机啊！

这台简单的脚踩踏板缝纫机是买给我外婆在一九二零年的。在当时，它就像一件艺术品，它身上的黑漆闪闪发亮。当不使用它的时候，它会放在一个很美丽的橡木柜橱里，这台缝纫机就像脚踏自行车一样，不用电力驱动，脚踩就行了。

我的外婆用这台缝纫机给她的十三个孩子做衣服，就好像"疯狂的兔子"，这台缝纫机就是停不下来。我的外婆去世以后，这台缝纫机就传给我的母亲，我的母亲很喜爱和珍惜它。我的母亲虽然不用给她的孩子做衣服，但她经常用它来修改衣服。

有一年，我们决定送一台电动缝纫机给母亲作为惊喜，我们想这样做可以让她的生活轻松一点。母亲试用了新缝纫机几次，很快又开始用回那台旧缝纫机了。

我的母亲去世以后，我的父亲不愿意放弃这台缝纫机，就把它放在客厅的一个角落里作为一个纪念。我的父亲再结婚了，他的新娘带来了新家具，其中包括一台电动缝纫机，那台旧缝纫机就序放在地下室了。

每年夏天，当我去探望我的父亲，我会看到那台旧缝纫机。越来越旧，每年我都会问我可不可以把它带回渥太华。有一年，我父亲给了我一个惊喜，把这台旧缝纫机给了我。回到了渥太华，我才意识到这台缝纫机看起来是多么的悲哀啊。

过了夏天，我丈夫去见了一个古物商，这个古物商同意重新复原这台旧缝纫机。就在圣诞节前夕，有人敲了我家的门，给我们送来了一台美丽的、复原了的缝纫机。

每一次，当我走到我的饭厅，我会看到一台很可爱的旧缝纫机，我会想起我的外婆和我的母亲。我的女儿，她住在一幢一六〇年旧的房子，这房子在Pefn。她告诉我她已经挑好了一个完美的位置来放这个"望欠"就等着我把这台旧缝纫机传给她。

Language : Chinese
Translated by : ???

My Reel Life

"[The television is] an invention that permits you to be entertained in your living room by people you wouldn't have in your living room."
David Frost

"Television is the triumph of machine against people."
Fred Allen

"if it weren't for Philo T. Farnsworth, the inventor of television, we'll still be eating frozen radio dinners."
-Johnny Carson

These are just three quotes taken from the endless pool of thought regarding television. I agree with all there of them, after truly encountering the marvel of the tube on a summer day several years ago.

I discovered a goldmine of humour, drama, mystery, and instant-gratification news. Television has successfully shown me the world in a whole new light. Along with the company of TIVO, tv.com and The TV Guide, I was on the path to Neverland. Little did I know I would be so bewildered that I would be spending the rest of summer days popping popcorn and flipping channels. All was fine and dandy until the summer break came to an end and I had to face the fearful faces of teachers and homework assignments, and finally wave goodbye to my true-blue TV. I wasn't ready to do so, after all, my journey was hardly over: Jeanie[*] is still locked inside the closed safe which will be sent into space, the finale of (insert television show here) is two hours long, and Wentworth Miller's TV brother[*1] still hasn't escaped his wrongful persecution. Missing any of them is not an option, so my title page would have to wait until tomorrow. And the next day would lead me unto a whole new adventure until the teacher calls home about the title page that is about 2 months overdue. But what would happen to the comatose Marlena on The Days of Our Lives[*2]? Will Gary on The Biggest Loser[*3] shed any weight this week? I just know that if I don't know who Donald Trump is going to fire next Thursday[*4] I would regret for the rest of my television-less life. I wonder if I could watch

TV and finish my project at the same time? Multi-tasking should be easy as 1-2-3.

After all was said and done, I was content to quit my addiction and face the world without the confinements of my TV. The tube is not for the weak of heart, but if you name me a day of the week, I would be glad to list you a number of worthwhile shows from 3:00 to primetime.

Notes:

*Jeanie – played by Barbara Eden on "I dream of Jeanie"

Jennifer Sun, Grade 8 Student

[*1] Prison Break – A man throws himself in jail to help his wrongfully-accused brother escape, on Monday 8/7, networks Global and FOX

[*2] The Days of Our Lives – popular daytime soap opera, on 12/1 weekdays, network NBC.

[*3] The Biggest Loser – weight-loss reality show where contestants compete with one another to win a quarter of a million dollars by losing the most weight, coming back soon on NBC.

[*4] The Apprentice – Billionaire Donald Trump seeks for his next right-hand man/woman. Moved from Thursdays to Monday 9/8 on NBC.

电视和我
豪桑小学写作论文集
珍妮佛 8 年级 2 班

"电视让你得到娱乐在你的客厅里，从人们你不会让进你的客厅里。"

-大卫 弗洛斯特

"电视是机器的成功。"

- 佛瑞德 艾伦

"如果没有法恩斯沃思（电视发明者），我们还会在吃冷冻广播晚餐。"

- 约翰尼 卡森

这些是三个不同的观点关于现代电视。我跟这些观点都同意，因为一件几年前发生的事。

电视立即可以给我喜剧，戏剧， 远动， 和新闻。加上电视录影机（TIVO)，电视节目查询, 和 tv.com 的帮助，我发现了电视。所以，整个夏天，我在做爆米花，然后换电视台。但是到夏天过去了的时候，我必须跟电视说再见。

我不想干此事：姬妮*1 还在铁箱子里锁着，＿＿＿＿＿＿＿电视节目的结尾是两个小时长，而且迈克尔-斯科菲尔德的哥哥*2 还没从监狱里逃出来那，我怎能停止看？电视制作者们把结尾写的扣人心弦，为了让我忘写作业。下一天又有更多节目我*必须*得看，作业就得再拖几天，得到老师开始着急："为什么你的作业还是没完成？"但是昏睡了的玛蕾娜*3 会怎么办？《大减肥》的加里能不能减 20 磅？而且我要是不知道谁唐纳 川普解雇这星期*4，我会后悔的。可不可以一边写作业，一边看电视；两全其美...

我的电视风波刮走了后，我是非常高兴我可以会到我的正常生活。但是你要知道今晚黄金时间有什么好节目，我会一个不落的告诉你。

---

*1 -《我梦见姬妮》：电视台 Deja-view
*2 -《越狱》：电视台 FO X 和 Global
*3 - Days of Our Lives (美国最著名的肥皂剧集之一)：NBC
*4 -《学徒》：电视台 NBC 和 Global

Language: Chinese
Translated by: Jennifer Sun, Grade 8 Student

My Family

I have a little brother. His name is Tim. He is two and a half years old.
I play hide-and-seek with him. In the summer, my family likes to go
to the park together. I also like to go swimming. One day, I will teach
my little brother how to swim. My family is loving.

Justin Xia, Kindergarten Student

我有一个小弟弟，他的名字叫 Tim。他两岁半了。我常和他玩捉迷藏。夏天里，我们全家喜欢一起去公园玩。我也喜欢游泳。将来有一天，我要教我的小弟弟怎样游泳。

我的家庭充满了爱。

夏加文

Language : Chinese
Translated by : ???

The Hat of a R.C.M.P.

Would you be interested in learning about my great-great-grandpa's R.C.M.P hat? It looks exactly like the one above. It was created with soft beige felt. It has a wide brim with a black stripe above it. Do you appreciate how the hat looks?

My great-great-grandfather was named William Walter Assheton-Smith. He came to Canada from England on a wee little raft for seven days and seven nights. He came to Alberta on an unidentified route. There he signed up for the Royal Canadian Mounted Police (R.C.M.P.) and got the hat. W.W. Assheton-Smith was my great-great-grandfather.

The hat is awfully special to my family, here's why. First, it is very old, over a hundred years old. Second, it's an artifact since it belonged to one of the first R.C.M.P. Third, it will be in the family for a noticeably long time. That's why the hat is special to my family.

Here's where the hat is located now. The hat is in an old fashioned and furry rumpus room. It hangs by its strap on the wall behind a dull bar counter. The rumpus room belongs to my grandma. The hat is now there.

Conor Assheton-Smith, Grade 3 Student

一顶皇家骑警的帽子

你一定感兴趣我家曾祖父一一位皇家骑警的警帽吧？它正如上面这幅画里的一模一样。它是由很软的呢毡子做成的，还有一圈宽宽的里边框。你欣赏这顶帽子的外观吗？

我的曾祖父名叫威兼·沃尔特·阿希顿·丝密斯。他是乘座一种非常小的竹筏子经过了七天七夜从英格兰来到加拿大的。他来到了阿尔白塔的一条不知名的小路上，在那里加入了皇家骑警队，得到了那顶皇家骑警帽的。那时的阿希顿·丝密斯就是我的曾祖父。

这顶帽子在我家里是非同寻常的。首先，它有很古老的历史，至少一百多年了。其次，它是用手工制造的，它属于一名最早期的皇家骑警。第三，它被遗传至我们家这一代有很久很久远的历史了。这就是为什么它对我们家如此的特殊。

想知道这顶帽子现在何处，在我们家有一间非常古老的娱乐室。娱乐室把台的后墙上挂着很多东西。娱乐室是属于我的祖母的。帽子就挂在那儿的墙上。

Language: Chinese
Translated by: ???

My Missing Part

All these years I felt as if I was missing something. It felt like I had a hole in me waiting to be filled and I knew that day was coming soon.

It's 5:00 a.m. and I just woke up. I'm not tired but excited because today was the day I'm leaving Canada! My parents emigrated from China to Canada 21 years ago. Now we are going back but only for vacation.

My head pushed against the seat as the airplane rose up into the morning sky. This was my first time on an airplane. I gazed out the window with excitement and saw the ground slowly disappear. I sat in my seat, thinking how it would be like to live in China for two whole months, meeting my other cousin, uncle, and aunt for the first time, visiting the Forbidden City and the Great Wall of China.

When we finally arrived in Guangzhou, I could barely find the strength to move and couldn't wait to go to sleep. As my family walked out of the air-conditioned airplane I felt an incredible wave of heat go pass me, and I started to sweat. Once we met up with my uncle, aunt and cousin my grandma burst into tears, because she got to see her son which is my uncle after 21 years. My brother and I both gave our cousin a hug. After all the hugs, crying and handshakes were over we went to their apartment, took a shower and went to bed.

A couple of weeks later my family, except my grandma, went to Shanghai. When we were in Shanghai we went to many places that talked about herbs and tea. There was one jewelry store that only sold pearls. They even let us keep one! The store had everything made from pearls necklaces, rings and even animals made from pearls. After we went to Shanghai we flew to Beijing, the capital of China. In Beijing I went into the Forbidden City which was the king's palace. The palace was huge, larger than a neighbourhood! All the rooftops of the buildings were a very bright yellow and had multiple designs under it. I also saw the throne, the royal stamp and the underground graves that belonged to the kings. Then I went to the Great Wall of China! It was amazing; the whole wall was built on top of mountains with grey blocks as big as your head. The Great Wall was also very wavy.

When we came back from Beijing it was almost time to go back to Canada, because school was starting soon. I spent the last couple of weeks with my cousin and my brother going to many places to have fun, like to the arcade.

After I came back from China I felt complete, the hole had been filled after many years.

Stanley Tom, Grade 8 Student

若有所失　　　　　　　　　　　作者: 史丹尼

这些年来我总觉若有所失， 像是内心有个空洞有待填满， 我知道这一天快要来临。

今天凌晨五时， 我刚睡醒， 并不感到疲倦， 反倒是兴奋， 因为今天正是我要离开加拿大的日子！我的父母在二十一年前从中国移民到加拿大， 现在我们回去， 只是为渡假而已。

当飞机直冲云霄之际， 我的头紧靠著椅背， 这是我有生以来第一次乘搭飞机， 我兴奋地望出窗外， 看到地面渐渐地在眼前消失。 我坐在座位上， 想到将如何在中国度过整整两个月的时间， 首次与我的表哥、 叔叔和阿姨会面， 及游览紫禁城和万里长城。

我们终于抵达广州， 我卷得无力再动了， 恨不得能快点睡觉。 当我们一家步出有空调的飞机后， 我感到一阵热浪漫过我身， 热得开始流干。 当我们一见到叔叔和表哥， 祖母不禁涌出泪来。 因为她事隔了二十一年后才有机会见到她的儿子， 就是我的叔叔。 我和弟弟给表哥一个拥抱。 在一番拥抱、 哭泣和握过手后， 我们一起到他们的住所， 淋浴后便入睡了。

数星期后， 除了祖母外， 我和家人一起到上海去。 在上海， 我们到过很多人们常讲论草药和茶的地方。 那儿有一间只售珍珠的珠宝店， 他们竟送了一粒珍珠给我们呢！这店铺的颈炼、 耳环， 甚至动物都是用珍珠做的。 离开上海后， 我们飞到中国的首都　　　　　-　　　　　北京。 我们到过皇帝的皇宫　　　　　-紫禁城参观。 这皇宫十分宏伟， 比整个社区还要大呢！那些建筑物的屋顶全是鲜黄色的， 在其下更有多样化的设计。 我又看到属于皇帝的宝座， 皇帝印章和地下墓穴。 然后来到万里长城了， 多么了不起啊！整座城墙就是由一块块有如你的头那么大的灰石块砌在山顶上， 万里长城真的是波峦起伏啊！

当我们从北京回来时， 也是时候要回加拿大了， 因为学校快要开课了。 我和表兄及弟弟花了好个星期去过多地方， 就如逛商场， 玩得很开心。

从中国回来后， 我感到十分满足， 多年来内心的空洞终于被填满了。

Language: Chinese
Translated by: Ivy Tong

Hawthorne *Writes*
because everyone has a story...

YOUR FUTURE IS NOW

7.   Estonian - Eesti

Estonian

Estonian language is spoken by an estimated 1 million people around the world. Most of these people – Estonians - live in Estonia (part of the European Union), however, it is also spoken in Finland Latvia, Lithuania, Sweden, Australia, and Canada, to name a few countries. Estonian is part of the Finno-Urgic language family. Like Finnish, Estonian employs the Latin alphabet, in addition to which the Estonian alphabet contains letters õ, ä, ö and ü. The letters c, q, w, x and y are limited to proper names of foreign origin, and f, z, š, and ž appear in loanwords and foreign names only. Ä, ö, and ü are pronounced similarly to their equivalents in German, the language from which they were originally borrowed.

There are about 600,000 Estonians currently living in Estonia. Estonians are very proud of their language, heritage and culture, even with their small population.

Eesti

Eesti keelt räägitakse maailmas umbes ühe miljoni inimese poolt. Enamus eesti keele rääkijaid - eestlasi - elab Eesti Vabariigis . Eesti Vabariik kuulub ühe väikseima riigina Euroopa Liitu. Eesti keelt räägitakse ka Soomes, Lätis, Leedus, Rootsis, Austraalias ja Kanadas, kui nimetada mõned riigid. Eesti keel kuulub soome - ugri keelkonda. Just nagu soome keeleski, kasutatakse ka eesti keeles ladina tähestikku; lisaks on eesti keeles kasutusel täishäälikud õ, ä, ö and ü. Tähti c, q, w, x, ja y kasutatakse peamiselt võõrkeelsetes pärisnimedes, samuti tulevad tähed f, z, š ja ž ette vaid laen- ja võõrsõnades. Ä, ö ja ü hääldatakse sarnaselt saksa keele samalaadsetele häälikutele, sealt need häälikud algselt laenati.

Käesoleval ajal elab Eestis umbes 600 000 eestlast. Hoolimata väikesest rahvaarvust on eestlased väga uhked oma päritolu, keele ja kultuuri üle.

Language Description and Translation by: Jaan Altosaar, Grade 8 Student

Why My Grandfather Fought In World War Two

It was the year 1944 and my grandfather was very young. He went to fight in WWII for Estonia's freedom. When he was 22 he was forced to join the Soviet Army, which occupied Estonia. He ran away because the Soviet Army was against Estonia. He hid in a forest and secretly joined the German Army and fought for Estonia's independence. The Soviet Union won the war and my grandfather was sent to GULAG. He spent 14 years in Siberia, Vorkuta in a prison camp, mining and building railways. Stalin, who was the leader of the Soviets, died in 1953 and this is the reason why my grandfather came out of prison and escaped his life long sentence after the war. My grandfather met my grandmother, Rita Sarv, and they fell in love and got married. They had 4 daughters. One of them was my mom, Tiiu Sarv. The four daughters were raised in Estonia occupied by the Soviets. They fought for Estonia's independence too. Estonia gained independence in August, 1991. My grandfather died in September, 1991. He was very happy to see Estonia free again.

Raul Altosaar, Grade 3 Student

Miks minu vanaisa võitles Teises Maailmasõjas

Oli aasta 1944 ja minu vanaisa Jaan Sarv oli väga noor. Ta läks Teises Maailmasõtta Eesti vabaduse eest võitlema .

Kui ta oli 22 aastane, sunniti teda astuma Nõukogude Liidu Armeesse, mis okupeeris Eestit. Vanaisa põgenes sellest armeest, sest Nõukogude Liit võitles Eesti vastu. Ta peitis end metsa ja ühines salaja Saksa Armeega, et kaitsta Eesti iseseisvust.

Nõukogude Liit võitis sõja ja minu vanaisa saadeti vangilaagrisse, GULAG-i. Vanaisa veetis 14 aastat Siberis, Vorkuta vangilaagris, kus ta töötas kaevandustes ja raudtee ehitustöödel.

Stalin, kes oli Nõukogude Liidu juht, suri aastal 1953 ja see on see põhjuseks, miks minu vanaisa pääses talle mõistetud eluaegsest vanglakaristusest.

Mu vanaisa kohtas mu vanaema Riita Sarve, nad armusid teineteisesse ja lasid ennast laulatada. Neid õnnistati elusaatuse poolt nelja tütrega. Üks nendest tütratest ongi minu ema, Tiiu Sarv. Need neli tütart kasvatati üles Nõukogude Liidu poolt okupeeritud Eestis. Ka nemad võitlesid Eesti vabaduse eest.

Eesti saavutas oma taasiseseisvuse 1991. aasta augustis. Minu vanaisa suri 1991.aasta septembris.

Vanaisa oli väga õnnelik, et ta nägi oma elu lõpus vaba Eestit.

Language : Estonian
Translated by : Jaan Altosaar, Grade 8 Student

Boat Trip to Canada

I was five years old when we sailed from England to live in Canada. I remember my dad and our dog, Paddy, were there to wave my mom and my brothers and sisters and I off - he would be joining us later. The ship was HUGE and I stayed very close to my mother.

My older sister coaxed me to go on deck with her so I went. I trusted her, after all. There were crowds of people all around and she told me to go into the crowd to see if our mother had come on deck. I did not want to go without her but she said she would wait right where she was. I told her no but she said she would tell the captain I was being bad by not listening to her and that he threw bad children overboard for the sharks to eat. That really scared me so I did what she told me. I no sooner got to the edge of the crowd when I looked back. She was gone! What did I do? Well, I opened my mouth and began to wail at the top of my lungs. That sure got people's attention.

This lady came and took my hand and asked where my mother was and I told her I didn't know. After telling her my name, she found out where our cabin was and took me there but no-one was around. She left a note on the door for my mother and then she took me to a big room where an orchestra was playing and I had to sit quietly and listen for such a long time. I was soooooo bored!

My mother finally came and rescued me and my big sister got into such trouble.

Laura Cinkant, Grade 4 Teacher

Laevareis Kanadasse

Ma olin viieaastane kui me tulime Inglismaalt Kanadasse elama. Ma mäletan, kuidas mu isa ja meie koer Paddy olid lehvitamas mu emale, mu vendadele ja õdedele ja mulle – et hiljem meiega ühineda Laev oli hiigelsuur ja ma hoidsin end ema ligi.

Mu vanem õde julgustas mind laevalaele tulema, nii ma läksingi temaga koos.Ma usaldasin teda väga.Laevalael oli väga suur rahvaulk ja mu õde palus mul nende sekka minna ja vaadata, kas ka ema on üles tulnud. Ma ei tahtnud minna, kuid tema lubas oodata täpselt seal, kus ta seisis. Mina ütlesin ei, kuid ta ähvaradas mind, öeldes et ta räägib kaptenile kui paha ma olen.Ta lisas, et kapten viskab halbu lapsi üle parda haidele toiduks. See kohutas mind ja ma tegin mis ta käskis. Kui olin võtnud paar sammu, pöörasin ringi. Mu õde ei olnud seal. Siis avasin suu ja röökisin täiest kõrist. Muidug sain niimoodi endale teiste tähelepanu.

Üks proua võttis mul käest kinni ja küsis kus mu ema on, aga ma ei teadnud. Ma ütlesin enda nime, ja ta leidis meie pere kajuti üles, aga kedagi ei olnud kohal. Ta jättis kajutiuksele kirja teatega mu emale, öeldes kus me oleme. Siis ta viis mind ühte suurde saali kus orkester mängis ja ma pidin seal väga kaua vaikselt istuma ja kuulama. Mul oli väääääga igav.

Lõpuks mu ema tuli ja päästis mind ära ning mu vanem õde sai kõvasti pahandada.

Language: Estonian
Translated by: Jaan Altosaar, Grade 8 Student

Hawthorne *Writes*
because everyone has a story...

8. Finnish – Suomi

Of the 5 million people who speak Finnish, most live in Finland. Finnish is also spoken in other parts of the world, including Canada, Estonia, Norway, Russia, and Sweden.

Stories of Stone

Although it sounds strange, even weird to some people, I have to admit that I like cemeteries. I always have. The reasons for this are lodged in my childhood and have little to do with death, but rather a fascination with life.

My childhood home was beside a small cemetery that belonged to the Swayze family who had farmed the land since the 1790s. The Swayzes had been part of the Loyalist migration after the American Revolutionary War. In 1950, when my father purchased the lot which he built our house on from Cliff Swayze, the Swayze family cemetery contained about thirty graves, though some were unmarked.

The lichen covered tombstones held stories that I tried to understand. Family connections, early deaths, name changes — Sweayze became Swayze — Barnabas and Sarah outlived their children. Andrew was married three times. I would imagine their lives, playing out their stories in my mind.

At times the cemetery was a playground. Brian Swayze was my age, and if he could play hide-and-seek in his family burial ground with us, then it had to be alright. The time he knocked off the lamb's head from a child's marker, I remember thinking that it was not a proper place to be playing baseball, but we continued nevertheless.

Today the Swayze cemetery is being surrounded by the suburbs of Hamilton, and could be covered up by a Wal-Mart parking lot. It will always remain, for me, a visible presence of our pioneer past and a place of history.

Having had graves for neighbors is the reason I give for an ongoing interest in cemeteries. Whenever I travel, I enjoy exploring church yards and cemeteries. There is a soothing calmness in the presence of the tributes to the dead. There are mysteries to solve, stories to be told, and lives to imagine.

Today I live near the Beechwood Cemetery, an undiscovered gem, as it is also a beautiful landscaped garden. Straight lines of rigid stones are found, appropriately, only in the war veteran's area. The rest of the cemetery meanders through the lives of over 100 years of Ottawa's, and indeed Canada's, history. So many stories in stone for me to read. Often, families come and have personal celebrations near the graves of their loved ones. I am always wondering, as I stroll through, "why did someone carefully clean off a stone this Christmas? Why did someone leave Roger a half-full bottle of whiskey? Who keeps putting a basket of flowers on the statue of Dorothea?" Clearly, this cemetery is also full of life and the living, as well as remembering the past. Cemeteries, for me, remain places where life goes on, guided by the past and watched over by the dead who live on in their "stories of stone."

Lorayne de Mestral, Intermediate Teacher

Myonnan, etta olen aina ollut kiinnostunut vanhoista hautapaikoista, hautausmaista yleensa, joka saattaa kuulostaa joistakin oudolta, jopa hullulta. Kiinnostukseni syyt juontavat juurensa lapsuuteeni eika niilla ole mitaan tekemista itse kuoleman kanssa, painvastoin minua viehattaa haudattujen ihmisten elaman kertomukset.

Lapsuudenkotini sijaitsi pienen hautausmaan vieressa, jonka omisti Swayze-niminen perhe. Perheessa on oltu maanviljelijoita aina siita lahtien, kun ensimmaiset Swayzet muuttivat paikalle, osana loyalisti-siirtokuntaa American Revolutionary sodan jalkeen 1790-luvulla. Isani osti vuonna 1950 pienen maapalan Cliff Swayze'lta ja rakensi siihen talon. Siihen aikaan hautausmaa kasitti noin kolmekymmenta hautaa, monet niista olivat nimettomia.

Sammaleen ja jakalan peittamat hautakivet sisalsivat kertomuksia edesmenneitten ihmisten elamasta, joita tutkin ja yritin ymmartaa. Kuten sukupolvien perhesuhteet, nimien muutokset – Sweayze ja Swayze, Barnabas ja Sarah elivat kauemmin kuin kaikki lapsensa, ja Andrew solmi avioliiton kolme kertaa, pienta tietoa, josta paasin selville lukiessani hautakivia. Mielessani kuvittelin, minkalaista heidan elamansa saattoi olla aikanaan.

Joskus tapahtui niin, etta hautausmaasta tuli leikkikentta. Brian Swayze oli samanikainen kuin mina ja jos han sai luvan piiloleikkeihin perheensa omistamalla hautausmaalla, meilla muilla ei ollut siihen mitaan sanomista. Kunnes Brian vahingossa potkaisi pikkulapsen hautakiveen liittyvan karitsan patsaan maahan, muistan ajatelleeni, ettei ehka ole enaa soveliasta pelata pesapalloa nain pyhassa ymparistossa.

Talla hetkella Hamilton kaupungin liitosalueet ymparoivat Swayze hautausmaata, samalla kun Wal-Mart suunnittelee parkki-aluetta sen lahistolle. Minulle, henkilokohtaisesti, tama vanha hautausmaa edustaa historiaa - se on elava merkki uutisasukkaiden, pioneerien, menneisyydesta ja heidan elamastaan.

Haudat ja hautakivet ovat olleet minun 'naapureitani', mista johtunee jatkuva kiinnostukseni menneisyyteen. Ollessani matkoilla minulle tuottaa suurta mielihyvaa kavella kirkkomailla, tutkia hautakivia, silloin minulle tulee levollinen olotila. Hautakivet kertovat niin paljon, salaperaisia asioita, outoja asioita, kertomuksia, joita paikalle osunut kavelija voi ainoastaan kuvitella mielessaan.

Asun talla hetkella hyvin lahella Beechwood hautausmaata. Se on kaunis uhrilehto, puutarha, joka on jaanyt tavallaan tuntemattomaksi tai tutkimattomaksi helmeksi. Sotaveteraanien haudat muodostavat militaarisesti suorat rivit, kun taas muut haudat ovat kiemurtelevien kaytavien molemmin puolin. Yli 100 vuotta historiaa, menneisyytta on haudattu tanne. Omaiset tulevat tapaamaan poisnukkuneita rakkaita sukulaisiaan, kunnioittamaan heita ja muistelemaan heidan elamaansa. Kavellessani kaytavilla olen havainnut joitakin outoja seikkoja. Esimerkiksi, miksi joku ihminen kiilloitti huolellisesti Roger'in hautakiven viime jouluna ja jatti hanen haudalleen puolityhjan viskipullon? Enta kuka jatkuvasti tuo Dorothean patsaalle tuoreen kukka-asetelman?

Hautausmaat ovat minun mielestani paikkoja, joissa elama jatkuu menneisyyden opastuksella, poisnukkuneiden valvoessa 'kivikertomuksiaan'.

Language: Finnish
Translated by: ???

Hawthorne *Writes*
because everyone has a story...

9. German – Deutsch

Almost three-quarters of the 96 million people who speak German live in Germany, however; it is also spoken around the world in countries like Austria, Belgium, Poland, Switzerland, and Canada. An estimated 28 million people speak German as a second language.

The Mattie Scrapbook

"What would I want to save if my apartment was on fire?" This was the question I asked myself this morning.

I live in a nicely furnished apartment with lots of pictures on the walls and knick knacks that need to be dusted, but last night when I had a look around to find some item I could write about, I was left with a blank. However, the 'burning apartment' question did lead me to an immediate response this morning. The Mattie scrapbook must be saved.

What is a Mattie scrapbook you ask? The short answer: it is a scrapbook about my dog Mattie. Pretty obvious, isn't it? And yes, it is 'just' paper and pictures all bound together in a book. However the whole is greater than the sum of its parts. Not only is the subject of the scrapbook so important to me but so is how it was created. This scrapbook is infused with love by my mom who spent months nurturing this treasure. That is why this scrapbook has become my most cherished possession since the death of my most cherished companion 2 years ago.

Mattie and I met at my high school co-op placement at a veterinary clinic. I was 17 and she was 3 months old. She was to be 'put down' due to illness and lack of a good home. Isolated in a back room, the vets decided to nurse her to health for free and try to find her a home. She was salvageable. I finally met Mattie 3 weeks after her arrival at the clinic, when she was no longer contagious. It would be kind to say I found her appearance shocking. "What is she?" I asked the vet, with a little bit of dismay and bewilderment in my voice. "An Australian Shepherd, blue merle". So timid, unsure, feeble and uncoordinated was this odd little creature that it didn't take much convincing of my parents to allow her to visit our home for some much needed socializing after her weeks in isolation. After a weekend at our house, we weren't willing to give her back and she had found her new home.

I could fill entire books with stories of our 12 years together. Isn't that true of any family that includes a well-loved pet? Mattie, whose full name was actually Mathilda, was a travel companion, making journeys all over Canada with myself and my parents. She was an ambassador for dogs everywhere, winning over those unenviable folks out there who've "never really liked dogs". She was a role model for younger dogs in the family, showing them the ropes of how to be a good glutton and scavenger. And she was like a visit to the spa for the people around her. In Mattie's presence all of your stress, anxiety and anger melted away. I miss that about her. Fortunately when I miss her, the scrapbook is sitting on the table next to me and in moments I can be visiting with her again.

Amy Schaefer, Intermediate Teacher

Das Mattie Einkleblebuch

Was würde ich aus dem Feuer retten stünde meine Wohnung in Flammen....jene Frage hab ich mir heute Morgen gestellt.

Ich wohne in einer wunderschönen Wohnung mit Bildern an der Wand und ziemlich viel Krimskrams, der oft abgestaubt gehört, aber als ich gestern Abend versucht habe etwas darunter zu finden, dass es wert wäre, aus dem Feuer gerettet zu werden, war ich ohne Erfolg. Doch heute Morgen wußte ich, was gerettet warden muss. Das Mattie Einklebebuch.

Ihr werdet Euch fragen, was fragen was das Mattie Einklebebuch ist. Eine kurze Antwort dafür: es ist ein Einklebebuch über meinen Hund Mattie. Leuchtet ein, richtig? Und ja, es handelt sich „nur" um Papier und etwaige Fotos, alles zusammen in einem Buch. Im Ganzen jedoch ist es mehr als nur ein aneinanderreihen von Erinnerungen. Nicht nur der Inhalt des Einklebebuches ist wichtig für mich, jedoch wie es entstand. Das Einklebebuch ist voll gefüllt mit der Liebe meiner Mutter, die Monate investiert hat, um diesen Schatz zu kreieren. Darum wurde dieses Buch zu meinem liebsten Besitz seit dem Tod meines liebsten Begleiters vor zwei Jahren.

Ich habe Mattie während meines Highschool Praktikums bei einem Tierarzt kennen gelernt. Ich war 17 und Mattie war 3 Monate alt. Man wollte sie einschläfern, da sie krank war und man keinen guten Platz für sie finden konnte. Isoliert in einem Hinterzimmer wurde sie vom Tierarzt ohne Bezahlung gesund gepflegt und er wollte versuchen ihr ein zuhause zu finden. Sie war es einfach wert, sie zu retten. Ich traf Mattie dann endlich drei Wochen später, nachdem sie nicht mehr ansteckend war. Es wäre „nett" zu sagen, ich hätte ihr Erscheinung als schockierend empfunden. „Was für ein Hund ist sie?" fragte ich etwas bestürzt und verwirrt. „ Ein australischer Hirtenhund." So befangen, so unsicher, so schwach und so unkoordiniert war diese kleine Kreatur, dass ich es nicht viel Überzeugungskraft gebraucht hat, meine Elter zu überreden, sie für eine Woche mit nachhause zu nehmen, nachdem sie längere Zeit so isoliert gelebt hatte. Nach dem ersten Wochenende in unsrem Haus, wollten wir sie einfach nicht mehr zurückgeben und somit hatte Mattie ihr neues Heim gefunden.

Ich könnte viele Bücher schreiben über diese letzten 12 Jahre. Aber ergeht es nicht jeder Familie mit einem geliebten Haustier ähnlich? Mattie, die eigentlich Mathilda hieß, war ein Reisegefährte, kam mit uns durch ganz Kanada. Sie war ein Botschafter für all die anderen Hunde, winselte über all jene Menschen, die keine Hunde mögen. Sie war ein Vorbild für jüngere Hunde in der Familie, holte das Beste aus ihnen heraus. Sie war der Ruhepol, in ihrer Nähe konnte man entspannen. All der Zorn, der Stress schmolzen in ihrer Nähe einfach hinweg. Sie fehlt mir. Glücklicherweise liegt in einem solche Momente das Einklebebuch vor mir auf dem Tisch und sie ist mir ganz nahe.

Language: German
Translated by: Isabel Doppelreiter

The Important Things

There are many things in life I could thank my parents for: the value of education and responsibility, the courage to take on challenges, the knowledge that sport is a necessity, and the idea that we all live in a community and everyone must do their part to make it better. But, the most important thing my parents have given me is the understanding that being close to family is important; no matter how far away they are.

My grandparents live in Altona, a small community an hour outside of Winnipeg. And although my they live a 24hrs drive or 3hrs plane ride away, my sisters and I grew up visiting and spending time with them. Every second winter, my parents would pack up the car with children, Christmas presents, and warm clothes (it is very cold in Altona), and drive through snow storms to a small country house in Manitoba.

Every summer from the age of eight to fifteen, I would get on a plane, fly to Winnipeg, and spend a month on the farm with my grandparents. I was never homesick, and my grandparents made sure we were always busy. Picking fruits and vegetable from the garden, racing tractors, rolling on barrels, walking on stilts, tea and baby bottle parties, and riding motorcycles and horses are just some of the things we did to occupy our time. My sister and I also had the run of the local high school. My grandfather was the custodian, and when we would go with him to work, we would run the halls, do crafts in the art room, and climb the equipment in the gym. Throughout the week my father would practice a variety of songs, and then on Sunday we would head to church to see him sing in his choir. My grandmother is an amazing cook, and the good food was endless. My favourites are crepes, cherry soup, perogies, and fresh baked buns and cinnamon rolls. Everything and every moment seemed special.

Near the end of every visit I would take part in the Sunflower Festival parade. The costumes were great, and we would throw candy to everyone standing watching us go by. When I look back on my childhood, the time I spent with my grandparents was the most precious gift I received. Even though they did not live around the corner and I didn't see them every week, I feel that they were a huge part of who I became.

Terry Plumb, Grade 8 Teacher

Die wichtigen Dinge

Es gibt viele Dinge in meinem Leben, für die ich meinen Eltern anken kann: die Notwendigkeit einer Ausbildung und Verantwortungsgefühl, den Mut Herausforderungen gegenüber zu stehen, dem Wissen, dass Sport wichtig ist und der Einstellung, dass wir alle in einer Gemeinschaft leben und jeder seinen Teil dazu beitragen muss, um diese besser zu machen. Das wichtigste jedoch, das meine Eltern mir gelehrt haben, ist es das Verstehen, dass die Familie der Mittelpunkt ist, egal wie weit man voneinander entfernt ist.

Meine Großeltern leben in Altona, eine kleine Stadt eine Stunde entfernt von Winnipeg. Und obwohl dies eine 24 Stunden Autofahrt oder einen 3 Stunden Flug entfernt war, sind meine Schwester und ich oft bei ihnen gewesen. Jeden zweiten Winter haben meine Eltern das Auto mit Geschenken und warmen Sachen (es wird ziemlich kalt in Altona) gepackt und wir sind durch Schneestürme zu jenem kleinen Farmhaus in Manitoba gefahren.

Jeden Sommer vom Alter zwischen acht und fünfzehn Jahren, bin ich in den Flieger gestiegen und nach Winnipeg geflogen, um ein Monat in dem kleinen Farmhaus mit meinem Großeltern zu wohnen. Ich hatte niemals Heimweh und meine Großeltern haben sich vergewissert, dass mir nie langweilig wurde. Obst pflücken und Gemüse, Traktor fahren, auf Heuballen herum toben, auf Stelzen gehen, Tee Partys veranstalten, Motorrad fahren oder Pferde reiten, es gab immer etwas zu unternehmen. Meine Schwester und ich konnten uns auch auf dem örtlichen Schulgelände austoben, denn mein Großvater war dort der Hausmeister. Wir haben ihn zur Arbeit begleitet und sind dann auf den Gängen herum gelaufen, haben im Handarbeitszimmer gebastelt und im Turnsaal gespielt. Während der Woche hat mein Großvater verschiedene Lieder geübt und Sonntags sind wir dann in der Kirche gesessen und haben ihm als Mitglied des Chors zugehört. Meine Großmutter ist eine fantastische Köchin und das gute Essen blieb nie aus. Am allerliebsten sind mir Crepes, Kirschsuppe, Perogies, frisch gebackenes Brot und Zimtschnecken. Alles und jeder Moment schienen magisch zu sein.

Am Ende eines jeden Sommerbesuches nahm ich an der Sonnenblumenfestparade teil. Die Kostüme waren wunderschön und ich schmiss allen Zuschauern Süßigkeiten hin. Wenn ich an meine Kindheit zurück denke, dann erscheint die Zeit, die ich mit meinen Großeltern verbracht habe, die wertvollste zu sein. Obwohl sie nicht um die Ecke gewohnt haben und ich sie nicht jede Woche sehen konnte, spüre ich, dass sie ein großer Teil davon sind, was ich heute bin.

Language: German
Translated by: Isabel Doppelreiter

Hidden Eggs

My family loves to celebrate holidays. We have special traditions for each of the holidays, but my favourite by far is Easter. On Easter morning my family gets together at my parents' house. My brother, my sister and I get to do an Easter egg hunt! We are pretty competitive during the hunt (which is usually over quickly), but we always share the eggs at the end. After the egg hunt, we have a special brunch. I love celebrating Easter with my family!

Miss Stephanie Ettinger, Grade 1 Teacher

Eier verstecken

Meine Familie liebt es sämtliche Feiertage zu zelebrieren. Wir haben spezielle Traditionen für jeden Feiertag, aber am allerliebsten habe ich Ostern. Am Ostermontag trifft sich die ganze Familie bei meinen Eltern zuhause und mein Bruder, meine Schwester und ich machen uns auf, all die versteckten Eier zu finden. Wir treten eigentlich fast schon gegeneinander an (und meistens ist die Suche auch schnell wieder vorbei), aber geteilt wird am Ende immer. Nach dem Eiersuchen gibt es dann ein spezielles Brunch. Ich liebe es mit meiner Familie Ostern zu feiern.

Language: German
Translated by: Isabel Doppelreiter

What was That?

"What's that Mommy?" I asked with a quiver in my voice.

"It's nothing. Go to sleep," she reassured me. At that moment something swooped across the room in our cottage where our whole family lay trying to sleep.

"Daddy! What's that?"

"That? That's just the spirit of a farmer who lived here one hundred years ago. He comes to visit us from time to time." That really didn't help me a whole lot! Yes, my dad had told us many a ghost stories over the years, but never had I been so convinced of their truth as that night.

I whispered to my sister who was five years older than me and a very grown up ten year old, "Is it true? Are there really spirits living here?"

"It was just a flying squirrel," she replied from the top bunk. Phew, now I felt better. But wait! Flying squirrel? Squirrels don't have wings. How could it be a flying squirrel? These thoughts flew through my mind but I tried to convince myself that somehow my sister was right. After all she was the big one. I rolled over and eventually fell asleep.

I don't know how long I had been asleep when I heard an ominous sound. CRUNCH, CRUNCH, CRUNCH. It was coming from the cellar of the cottage where we kept the wood for the stove! "Maybe the spirit is upset that I didn't believe in him," I thought. A moment later I heard my mom and dad stirring and my dad got up with a groan.

"Not again," he muttered to my mom. I heard him get up, pull on his boots and trudge around the house to get to the cellar. Then I heard a terrific ruckus coming from under the house. I turned to my other sister. She was four years older than me so she would know if it was the spirit. Wouldn't she? "Do you think we upset the spirit again?" I asked.

"It's just the porcupine eating the stairs. Go back to sleep." I tried to sleep. I really did but, well, I couldn't. When my dad got back he reassured me that it was just a porcupine and that he had scared him away. What a relief!

"Um, Mommy?"

"Yes, what is it now?"

"I have to go to the outhouse and I'm scared. Will you come with me, please?" With a sigh she pulled on her boots as I danced around waiting. We stepped outside. It was so dark that you could see the most spectacular constellations. I knew all about the big dipper. This was not a time for star gazing though. I started to race toward the outhouse and then stopped dead in my tracks. There was a rustling in the bushes!

"Mommy, is it a bear?"

"No, the bears don't come this close to the house, don't worry." I pretended to believe her but I recalled a time when my sisters and I were exploring near the creek and I heard a noise in the woods. My sisters had rushed me back to the house telling me that it was just a cow. Well, I may have been only five years old, but I knew my sisters wouldn't have been that scared of a cow.

As I stood clinging to my mom in terrified fascination, a black and white creature about the size of a big cat sauntered out of the bushes. I knew what that was and it wasn't a bear. It was worse. My dad always said he wasn't afraid of bears but skunks? That was a different story. I had a really hard time waiting totally still until that stinky creature crossed in front of us. My mom warned me that it might spray us if we scared it. Finally it passed. I raced the rest of the way to the outhouse with my flashlight in hand. Moments later I came racing back out panting and jumping up and down pointing. "Snake!" I cried. At that, my mom and I just began to giggle. We laughed so hard we had tears rolling down our cheeks. What a night! And it was only half past midnight. We had at least six more hours to sleep!

Sandy Labonte, Grade 2 Teacher

"Ganz veraengstigt rief ich,"Mutti, Mutti hoerst Du dass?" "Es ist nichts. Kleines, nun schlaf mal endlich." In diesem Moment hoerte ich etwas durch den Raum huschen in unserem Wochenendhaus, wir schliefen alle in einem Zimmer.

"Papa! Was war das?"

"O, das war der Geist des alten Farmer's, der vor vielen, vielen Jahren in diesem Haus gelebt hat,"sagte er. " Der kommt von Zeit zu Zeit und geistert hier herum." Papa hatte uns schon des oefteren erzaehlt das der Mann in einem sehr kalten Winter nicht mehr heim gekommen war und man ihn nie gefunden hatte. Diese Geschichte half mir nicht viel mit meiner Angst in dieser Nacht. Papa erzaehlte oft tolle Geschichten, aber in heute glaubte ich ihm wirklich.

Ich fluesterte meiner fuenf Jahre aelteren Schwester ins Ohr, "ist das wirklich wahr"? Sind hier wirklich Geister?" Sie ist ja schliesslich mit zehn Jahren schon fast erwachsen, sie musste das doch wissen.

"Es ist nur ein fliegendes Eichoernchen", sagte sie. Das hoerte sich schon besser an. Aber gibt es wirklich fliegende Eichoernchen? Eichoernchen koennen doch nicht fliegen, aber sie musste das ja wissen, sie ist ja die grosse, kluge Schwester. Dann schlief ich beruhigt ein.

Ich weiss nicht wie lange ich geschlafen habe, ich wachte auf und hoerte ein Geraeusch ein Nagen und Kratzen, und diesmal kam es aus dem Keller, wo Papa das Holz fuer den Ofen aufbewahrte. Ist der Geist jetzt im Keller? dachte ich, ist er veraergert? Ploetzlich hoerte ich Mutti und Papa stoehnen, "was ist denn jetzt wieder los"? Papa stand auf, zog seine Gummistiefel an und ging in den Keller. Das war ein Laermen. Ich fragte meine andere Schwester (die vier Jahre aelter war) ob sie meinte dass dies der Geist des Farmer's sei."
"Es ist doch nur ein Stachelschwein das die Stufen annagt, du kannst ganz beruhigt schlafen, wir sind doch alle hier," sagte sie.
Als Papa aus dem Keller zurueck kam erzaehlte er uns, dass er ein Stachelschwein verjagt hat. Da war ich doch beruhigt.

"Mutti ich muss aufs Clo." Mitten in der Nacht auf den Donnerbalken, war immer ein Erlebnis und ich fragte Mutti ob sie mit mir geht. So, wir zogen unsere Stiefel an and gingen raus. Es war so dunkel und die Sterne funkelten so herrlich wie man es in der Stadt nie erlebt. Aber es war nicht die richtige Nacht um Sterne zu bewundern. Ich ging in die Richtung des Clo's und blieb ploetzlich wie angewachsen stehen. Ich hoerte Geraeusche im Wald in Richtung Donnerbalken.

"Mutti, ist das ein Baer?"
"Die Baeren kommen nicht so nahe ans Haus",sagte sie. Aber ich konnte mich daran erinnern das meine Schwestern einmal im Wald in der naehe des Baches einen Baer gehoert hatten, mir aber sagten sie es war eine Kuh. Ich war nur fuenf Jahre alt, aber ich wusste doch das man vor einer Kuh keine Angst zu haben braucht.

Ich hielt Mutti's hand ganz feste, und was sahen wir, ein schwarzweiss gestreiftes Tier, das kannte ich.. Ein Stinktier, kam aus dem Wald. Es war also kein Baer. Es war noch schlimmer. Papa hat immer gesagt das er Baeren nicht fuerchtet, aber Stinktieren aus dem Weg geht. Wir standen ganz still bis das Tier verschwunden war, schliesslich wollten wir ja nicht angespritzt werden. Es lief tief in den Wald und ich musste jetzt dringend zum Clo mit meiner Taschenlampe. Kaum war ich dort passierte wieder wass, ich rannte wie der Blitz zur Mutti und schrie" Schlangen, Schlangen. " Da fing Mutti an zu lachen, und ich fing an zu griensen.. Wir lachten beide biss uns die Traenen kamen.

War das eine Nacht zum erinnern?

Es war nach Mitternacht und wir hatten noch sechs Stunden schlaf bis wir fischen gingen.

Language: German
Translated by: G. Gottleb

The First Time I visited my Aunt

This is the first time I have ever visited my aunt, uncle and cousin. I could not visit them before because they live all the way in the U.S.A. I also have other relatives living in Europe. I would have come sooner but I did not have a passport to go over the border. My aunt once visited my family before we went and saw her in the U.S.A. My family and I made a two-week plan to visit my aunt in July on my cousin's birthday. I was very excited about the trip. My mom packed for the trip. I packed books, toys, crayons, a harmonica and an enormous plastic dolphin. It took eight hours on the bus from Canada to the U.S.A. The ride seemed long but I still had a really good time on the ride. We were tired but happy when we arrived to my aunt's house. My uncle told lots of jokes about my dolphin and he promised he would take me to the ocean. Every night my aunt would pull a prank on me. Sometimes the cats pulled pranks on us. The cats brought a mouse into the house and hid it in a shoebox. Many evening the cats would chase the mouse around the house until one night the mouse was caught and found in the cat's mouth. Everybody was screaming and running around. My dad and uncle caught the cat with the mouse and brought them outside. After all the excitement we all went to bed. During our trip we received many visitors and went on many excursions to fun places like Chucky Cheese and Cosmic Adventures. During our trip we also ate Bosnian food, listened to Bosnian music and spoke our native Bosnian language. The visit to my aunt's house was great fun. I can't wait until my next visit to my aunt's house.

Benjamin Cejvan, Grade 2 Student

Als ich zum ersten Mal meine Tante besucht habe

Dies war das erste Mal, dass ich meine Tante, meinen Onkel und meine Kousine besucht habe. Ich konnte sie zuvor nicht besuchen, da sie weit weg in den Staaten wohnen. Ich habe auch Verwandte, die in Europe wohnen. Ich hätte meine Tante schon früher besucht, aber ich hatte keinen Pass. Meine Tante hat uns einmal in Kanada besucht, bevor wir in die Staaten gereist sind. Meine Familie und ich haben geplant zum Geburtstag meiner Kousine im Juli für zwei Wochen nach Amerika zu fahren. Ich war sehr aufgeregt. Meine Mutter hat all unsre Koffer gepackt. Ich hatte Bücher, Spielzeug, Kreiden, eine Harmonika und einen riesigen plastik Delphin in meinem Koffer.Die Busfahrt in die Staaten hat acht Stunden gedauert. Es war zwar eine lange Fahrt, aber ich hatte trotzdem Spaß. Wir waren müde, aber sehr glücklich als wir endlich ankamen. Mein Onkel hat wegen meinem Delphin sehr herum gealbert und er hat mir versprochen, dass er mit mir zum Meer fahren wird.

Wir haben jeden Abend damit verbracht uns gegenseitig rein zu legen und eines Abends hat die Katze uns ganz schön erschreckt. Sie versteckte eine Maus in einer Schuhschachtel. Sie hatte schon längere Zeit versucht, diese Maus zu fangen und eines Abends hatte sie es geschafft. Mein Vater und mein Onkel haben die Katze samt Maus dann gefangen und sie wieder nach draußen gebracht. Nach all der Aufregung sind wir gleich schlafen gegangen.Wir haben während unsres Aufenthaltes sehr viel unternommen. Einmal sind wir zu „Chucky Cheese" und „Cosmic Adventures" gefahren. Wir haben viel bosnisches Essen gegessen, haben bosnische Musik gehört und haben unsre Muttersprache Bosnisch gesprochen.

Ich kann es kaum erwarten meine Tante wieder zu besuchen, denn ich hatte so viel Spaß.

Language: German
Translated by: Isabel Doppelreiter

Hawthorne *Writes*
because everyone has a story...

YOUR FUTURE IS NOW

10.　Hindi – हिन्दी

Hindi

Hindi is the national language of the world's largest democracy – India. In this land of 1.3 billion people, there are 18 official languages, out of a total of 325 spoken languages and 1652 dialects. An estimated 180 million people speak Hindi throughout India, Nepal, South Africa and even Uganda. Another estimated 120 million people speak it as a second language throughout the Philippines, Singapore, United Arab Emirates, United Kingdom, and Canada.

Hindi is a phonetic language and is derived from Sanskrit, which was the language of the 5,000 year old ancient civilization of India.

Hindi script is called "Devnagri" and is written from left to right. There are mainly 11 vowels and 33 consonants. There is a systematic way to create and represent all the sounds produced by the human voice using the basic sounds represented by these 44 alphabets, and various permutations and combinations of consonants and vowel. This immense bank of sounds is quite useful in transcribing with ease the words spoken in any language. There is no similarity of alphabets with other languages of the world except for some of the other languages of India.

हिन्दी

विश्व के सबसे बड़े प्रजातन्त्र - भारत की राष्ट्रभाषा हिन्दी है।   1.3 अरब लोगों के इस देश में 18 सरकारी भाषाएं हैं, 325 बोलचाल की भाषाएं हैं और 1,652 उप-भाषाएं हैं।   लगभग 1,800 लाख लोग हिन्दी बोलते हैं भारत, नेपाल, दक्षिण अफ्रिका और युगान्डा में!   इसके अलावा लगभग 1,200 लाख लोग इसे बोलते हैं दूसरी भाषा के तौर पर, फिलिपीन्स, सिंगापुर, संयुक्त अरब एमरीटस युनायटेड किंगडम और कनाडा में।

हिन्दी एक ध्वन्यात्मक भाषा है और उसकी उत्पत्ति हुई है संस्कृत से, जो कि 5,000 वर्ष पुरानी भारतीय सभ्यता की भाषा थी।

हिन्दी की लिपि देवनागरी कहलाती है और या बांयें से दाहिनी और लिखी जाती है।   इसमें मुख्यतः11 स्वर और 33 व्यंजन होते हैं।   इन मूल 44 वर्णों में, मानव की आवाज द्वारा जनित हर ध्वनि की सृष्टि और प्रस्तुति की एक सुव्यवस्थित क्षमता है। इस क्षमता में सम्मिलित हैं स्वर और व्यंजन के सम्मिश्रश के आन्यान्य तरीके, अर्ध-व्यांन, और पूर्ण अ अर्धि र की ध्वनि के साथ व्यंजनों का सम्मिश्रश। ध्वनियों का यह असीम भंडार, किसी भी भाषा के शब्द को सरलता से लिपिबध्द करने की क्षमता रखता है।

हिन्दी के वर्ण, संसार की किसी भी अन्य भाषा से मिलते-जुलते नहीं हैं, सिवाय भारत की ही कुछ अन्य भाषाओं के।

Language Description and Translation by: Aruna Gupta, International Language Teacher

When I Went to a New School

When I came to Canada I was afraid. Then I joined a school called Hawthorne Public School. I thought I wouldn't understand English very well. The day was September 10th. I was joining Ms. Ettinger's class. I was really scared. But I got to know them well. I started going to ESL with Ms. Penney. We got to read books. At recess time, I went to the Grade 3 yard to see my brother. I thought I was allowed to go there, but I wasn't. Then I went to the Grade 1 yard. I was happy to know where I should stay and I met a nice friend. I felt great and happy because I was a part of the class. I didn't feel afraid anymore. I still missed my old school a little bit, but I like Canada's schools better.

Shwetank Nath, Grade 3 Student

जब मैं नई स्कूल में गया

जब मैं कैनाडा आया तो मैं डर लगता था। उसके
बाद मैं हैथोन स्कूल में आये लेकिन मुझे
अन्ग्रेजी बोलना उतने अच्छा नहीं आता था.
सितंबर १० दिन था जब मैं इस स्कूल में आया
था। डर को बहुत ही लगा। पहले मैं अन्ग्रेजी
सीखा और फिर अपने दोस्त बनाने लगा
और दिन अच्छा लगने लगा। पुराने स्कूल की
याद तो आती थी लेकिन ये स्कूल अच्छा लगने
लगा।

Language : Hindi
Translated by : Somran Kumar Roy, Grade 8 Student

A Very Important Memory To Me

On the warm, sunny morning of August 15 2005 at 8:30 am I took a bus to the Civic hospital to visit my newborn baby sister! I searched over the whole baby wing until I found her. I was so jubilant! I finally became a big sister!

From that day on whenever someone talked about my sister I loved it. I always kept smiling at her and she kept smiling, giggling and laughing at me. Everybody in the house was very cheerful after that.

On the third day visitors and gifts started coming in. There even my friends Nikita and Anjali's families came to visit. Everyday I woke up at 5:30 in the morning and then go to visit them at the hospital.

She looks like me! She has brown eyes and the same round face as me. She is glamorous, fair and striking. She even has a lot of curly hair. Our mother says that if we were born a year a part we would look like twins.

When Riya came home for the first time my grandfather took me Loblaws to buy flowers. But when we got home Riya was already there! We showed her the whole house. And gave her new toys to play with. I had a fun day the first time she came home.

The first few days Riya came into this world were the most unforgettable days of my life. They were also the most special days of my life . The first time I saw Riya I thought to myself, "This is it, this is my new life that's beginning as a new person: a new person called a big sister." Riya's birth is the most unforgettable moment of my life. And I hope that big sister and big brothers everywhere will make the first few days of their brothers or sister birth the most unforgettable moments of their lives as well.

Riya's birth is a memory that I don't want to or never will forget.

Tanvi Sharma, Grade 4 Student

मेरी बहुत महत्वपूर्ण स्मृति- तानवी शर्मा

15 अगस्त 2005 की एक गरम, धूपवाली सुबह के 8:30 बजे मैं बस लेकर अपनी नवजात छोटी बहन को देखने सिविक अस्पताल पहुंची! मैंने बच्चों वाला पूरा भाग छान मारा जब तक कि मैंने उसे ढूंढ न निकाला। मैं बहुत प्रफुल्लित थी। आखिरकार मैं बड़ी बहन बन गई थी!

उस दिन के बाद से जब भी कोई भी मेरी बहन के बारे में बात करता, मुझे बहुत अच्छा लगता था। मैं हर समय उसकी ओर मुस्कुराती रहती और वह भी मेरी ओर मुस्कुराती, किलकिलाती और हंसती रहती। उसके बाद से घर में हर कोई प्रसन्नचित रहता।

तीसरे दिन मिलने वाले और उपहार आने शुरु हुए। मेरी मित्र निकिता और अंजलि के परिवार भी वहां मिलने आए। हर रोज मैं सुबह 5:30 बजे उठती और उससे मिलने अस्पताल जाती।

वह तो मेरी तरह दिखती है! उसकी भूरी आंखें है और मेरे जैसा गोल चेहरा। वह मोहक, गोरी और प्रभावशाली है। उसके बहुत सारे घुंघराले बाल भी हैं। हमारी मां का कहना है कि यदि हम दोनों एक साल आगे-पीछे पैदा हुए होते तो जुड़वां लगते।

जब रिया पहली बार घर आई, मेरे दादा मुझे फूल खरीदने के लिये लौबलौज़ ले गए। लेकिन जब हम घर पहुंचे तो रिया वहां पहले ही पहुंच चुकी थी! हमने उसे पूरा घर दिखाया। और उसे खेलने के लिये नए खिलौने दिये। जिस दिन वह घर आई वह मेरे लिये मनोरंजक दिवस था।

रिया के इस संसार में आने के बाद के पहले कुछ दिन मेरे जीवन के अत्यधिक अविस्मरणीय दिन थे। वे मेरे जीवन के सबसे ज्यादा विशेष दिन भी थे। पहली बार जब मैंने रिया को देखा था, मैंने मन में सोचा, "बस यही है सब कुछ, यही मेरी नई जिन्दगी है जो कि एक नए व्यक्ति की तरह शुरु हो रही है : नया व्यक्ति जिसे बड़ी बहन कहते हैं।" रिया का जन्म मेरे जीवन का सबसे बड़ा अविस्मरणीय क्षण है। और मुझे आशा है कि सभी जगह बड़ी बहनें और बड़े भाई भी अपने भाइयों या बहनों के जन्म की शुरुवात के कुछ दिन अपने जीवन के अत्यधिक अविस्मरणीय क्षण बनाएंगे। रिया के जन्म की स्मृति को ना कभी भूलना चाहूंगी ना कभी भूल सकती हूं।

Language: Hindi
Translated by: Aruna Gupta, International Language Teacher

Hawthorne *Writes*
because everyone has a story...

YOUR FUTURE IS NOW

11.   Hebrew – עברית

Hebrew

Hebrew is spoken by an estimated 5 million people around the world. Most of these people live in Israel, however, it is also spoken around the world in Australia, Canada, Germany, Palestinian West Bank and Gaza, and the United States.

עברית

עברית היא שפה שמדוברת בארץ
חל מ... אליעזר בן יהודה... בארצם. המושבים
שפות אחרות ... ישראל, אולם השפה של
מדוברת אוכלוסיה, קצת ... ...
כמה הארצית, בכלל ובאיזורות הברית.

Language Description and Translation by: Mr. Piotrkowski

Pesach

There are so many holidays at Hawthorne. For example Pesach is a Jewish holiday celebrating freedom. Pesach translated into English is "Passover".

The story of Pesach starts off in the year 1200 BC, in Egypt. The Jewish people had been slaves for 400 years. When God told Moses to ask Pharaoh to release the Jewish people, Pharaoh refused and God brought down the ten plagues on Egypt. The last plague was the killing of the first-born Egyptian males. This was because Pharaoh had ordered that all the first born Jewish males be killed. In order to tell which houses were Jewish, God told the Jews to put lambs blood on the door posts so that the "Angel of Death" would Passover their homes. The Jewish people had to leave Egypt quickly, which resulted in the bread not having time to rise.

We celebrate Pesach by having a meal with family and friends. During the meal we read the story of Pesach. We also eat symbolic food: unleavened bread, called "Matzah", to remember that the Jews left Egypt in a hurry and the bread did not have time to rise, horseradish to remember the bitterness of slavery, green vegetables dipped in salt water to remind us of the tears of the Jewish slaves and the circle of life.

We sing songs that thank and praise God for freeing us and we also thank God for bringing us to this time

Finally we express a wish that we may be able to go to Jerusalem to celebrate Pesach the following year.

Sarah Piotrkowski, Grade 8 Student

כי הרבה מאת חכים ההגידון, כפי ושאנה, פסח בההגד
גם יהודים חלקים חרות. פסח מתורים בולשית
ב "Passover".

הספור פ פסח מת חיים בארמון פני הדור הזה
מצרים. רק עם היהודי היו צברים אם 400 שנה. כאשר
אמר משה לפרעה להרחרר את עם היהודי,
פרעה אומר לו, והבם הסיכו מות עשר המכות למצרים.
המכה הקיערינה היתה מכת הבכורות. המכה הקבשות
היתה תשובה לפרעה שהוא אמר לצוו בווה שכ הבנים
הזכורים היהודים יהורגו. בכ, לצאת בשויה התים כל בנים
יהודים, הפם אמר ליהודים פסים. כל בכח אם מצות
בתיהם כדי ש"מלאך המוות" יעבות לע הבתם. היהודים
היו מוכרחים לצות מצרים מאהרה וכח לעורהיה מספך
בצק לחם מצות.

ועתה, ווגים אות פסח בשביעת סורה לע מצה
וחברים, בבל מצוה פני הגרסים אות פסר הסח.
ועתה לע עולים מספים עם מצאת, פם פני
הומאן שקרוא "מצה" לפור שביות אבו אות
מצרים בממה וכו הסיך לחם שהתאית. אכיר פור
אות המריות לע צבוות. יהות בא נלת לפרירי פלו
סוד לתצות האבתהיהודים ועמכ החיים

אונן מרעים שירים של חורב וחגדה. ואלפים אנשי הפשע
סצורו מותי ורא סבגזיר, לזוגן הכה.

לפסוק מלוחו נפשים אוכל לגלם לירשים
פשת הגבא ורא לעלחה סוג הפסו.

Language: Hebrew
Translated by: Mr. Piotrkowski

Hawthorne *Writes*
because everyone has a story...

12.   Igbo – Igbo

Igbo is a language of Nigeria. It is spoken by an estimated 18 million people around the world.

Memories

One day, my whole family went to Toronto. There were so many people! We went on a really big boat that was mostly black with some red. The boat ride was not short, it was not long, it was kind of in-between. When we got to an island, it was really cool. There were trees and it was funny because there was a Pizza Pizza there, too.

In the park there were swans and ducks so we decided to feed them. When we were feeding them, the ducks ate most of the bread. When we walked further, we saw a bike and a garden that was very pretty. We also saw a beach.

It was time to leave the park but we went to the CN Tower before we headed home.

Cynthia Onukagha, Grade 4 Student

IHE NCHETAM MGBE GARA AGA

Otu ubochi, ezinulo anyi gara Toronto. Otutu ndi madu biakwara ebe ahu. Anyi gbara otu ugbo mmiri o bu etere agba ojii na agba uhe. Njem anyi n'ugbo mmiri ahu eteghi oke aka. Ugbo mmiri ahu buuru anyi gaa n'ala akoro nke mmiri gbara gburu gburu anakpo "island" n'asusu bekee. Ebe ahu mara mma nke ukuu. Enwere otutu osisi ndi mara mma eji cho ebe ahu mma ma ihe turum n'anya bu mgbe m'huru ulo ebe ana ere nri ana akpo Pizza Pizza n'ebe ahu.

Ebe ahu nwekwara ala ngwuri egwu mara mma eji ahihia n'acha ndudu na okoko osisi di iche iche cho ya mma. Enwe kwara otutu ntakiri ntakiri mmiri kwara akwa ebe odoguma na otu anumanu dika odoguma olu ya toro ogologo na acha ocha na egwu mmiri. Anyi tupuru ha ihe oriri n'elu mmiri, odoguma ndi ahu bu ndi riri otutu n'ime ihe oriri ahu. Mgbe anyi gatukwara n'ihu, anyi huru otu igwe, anyi hu kwara otu akuku ala mara mma nke ukuu ekeputara iche, akuru otutu okoko osisi n'ogbara n'ogbara. Anyi hukwara ebe ndi mmadu na no egwuri egwu n'onummiri ukwu di n'ebe ahu. Ugbua oge ilaghachi eruola, ma tutu anyi alaghachi ulo, anyi gara na CN Tower bu otu n'ime ulo kacha to ogologo n'uwa nile.

Language: Igbo
Translated by: Kate Onukagha

Hawthorne *Writes*
because everyone has a story...

13.   Inuktitut – ᐃᓄᒃᑎᑐᑦ

Inuktitut is spoken by an estimated 14 thousand people in Canada. Inuktitut means "like the Inuit." It is written using aboriginal syllabics.

A Family Treasure

Our family Treasure is a Qulliq which is an oil lamp. My grandmother got the oil lamp from her mother last summer. She gave it to her because she was special to her.

The Quilliq came from the land made out of a special stone. The special stone is only found in a few places up north. It is usually black.

My grandmother uses a flower called Arctic Cotton as a wick. She uses whale or seal blubber for the oil. It is used to cook and boil food. It keeps the house warm and gives light.

It is big and heavy and it's shaped like a half moon. It is a cozy feeling when it's lit.

Alex Kangok, Grade 4 Student

ᐃᓚᒌᑎᒍ ᐱᓐᓇᕆᔭᕗ

ᐃᓛᒌᑎᒍ ᐱᓐᓇᕆᔭᕗ ᖁᓪᓚᐅᕗᖅ, ᐅᖁᖅᓗᑦ ᖃᐅᒪᖁᑎ.
ᐊᓈᓇᑦᑎᐊᕐᒪ ᑑᑦᓱᖁᑦᑎᐊᕆᓚᑕᐅᖅ ᐊᓈᓇ ᒥᓂ
ᐊᐅᓯᐅᓚᐅᖅᑐᒥ. ᑐᓂᓚᐅᖅᑕᕗ ᐱᓐᓇᕆᒍᑎᐅ.
ᖁᓪᓚᖕ ᓴᓇᐅᒐᐅᕗᖅ ᓴᖑᓐᓂᖁᐊᓚᒃᓯᒥᓂᑐᖅ: ᓴᓈᖁᐊᓚᒃᓴᐃ
ᓇᓂᓯᐅᕆᓂᖁᕗ ᑕᒃᐸᓂ ᖁᑦᑎᒃᑐᒥ ᐊᒥᖂᕆᑦᑐᓂ ᓄᓇᓂ.
ᑭᖅᓂᑯᓯᓐᓂᖅᓯᐅᕗ.
ᐊᓈᓇᑦᑎᐊᕋ ᐊᑐᕌᖑᕗᖅ ᕿᔪᑎᓂ (ᓛᒃᒎᓯ) ᐃᐸᖕᒃᑲᓂ.
ᖄᓗᒃᑯᐅ ᓇᑦᑎᐅᓯᓂ [illegible] ᐅᖁᐊᓂ
ᐅᖁᖅᑲᓂ. ᐆᖅᓚᐅᕈᑕᐅᕈᓐᖑᕗᖅ ᐊᒻᒪ
ᖃᓚᑎᑦᑎᕈᑕᐅᓂᖅᑲᓂ. ᐃᒡᓗᒥ ᐅᖑᑎᑦᑎᕈᓐᖑᕗᖅ
ᐊᒻᒪ ᖃᐅᒪᒋᔭᐅᓂᖅᑲᓂ.
ᐊᕐᕌᒍᕗᖅ ᐅᖁᒪᐃᑐᖅᑲᓂᒃ, ᑕᖅᑭᐅ
ᐊᕐᕋᒍᑎᑐ ᐋᖅᑭᓯᒪᕗ. ᐃᑉᐱᒪᑎᑦᑐᒍ ᑲᔪᓐᓂᖅᑐᐊᓗ.
ᐋᓚᒃᓯ ᖁᐊᕐᑐᖅ

Language: Inuktitut
Translated by: Kim Kangok

What are we doing?

Sometimes I wonder why we are doing certain things. Have you ever wondered that? Why we kill, why we start wars, why we fight and yell over something as small as who is right about something you read...

When I say "kill", I know you probably think of guns, knives, and all of those horrible things we use for committing that retched crime. And the other thing you think about are the cold, still bodies of...Hold on, the bodies of what? Humans, animals, or plants? Okay, so you draw the line there. After all, cutting down plants and trees is not, and never has been, a crime, right? Who could possibly care about something like that? We have so much. So just how long will that last? Maybe a couple of centuries. How many trees were cut down in the last ten minutes? A million, a billion, more? I am not exaggerating, merely stating facts that most people know, and ignore.

We sit here, working or playing on the computer, watching television, eating, sleeping, and completely ignoring everyone who says things like this. We lock ourselves away, pretending that if we go to school, or go to our little jobs, then when we die we are going to be so proud of the undistinguished lives we lived. We say to ourselves that there is no point, or no time to go running around after little things like the forests.

Well, what about the rainforests? When cute little kindergarteners think about the rainforests, they think about toucans and frogs living in a dense, leafy terrain. How many adults would care to tell them that people are hacking the rainforest down to build pastures for cows, which are going to be turned into hamburgers for fast food restaurants? We humans, the superior beings, shall not be troubled by such inferior things. And if you protest, say that I am not being fair, that you do care about the rainforests, then why are you not doing anything?

Tons of animals live in the rainforests, and we cut their homes down. Perhaps not you in particular, but I can be almost positive that you are not "chomping at the bit" to help those who were there first. Sure, if you never do anything, it will not affect you. It will affect everybody that comes after you. In future generations, some little child will look at their parent and ask why you did not help, did not preserve the environment so that they could see it in all of it's' glory. And that poor parent will have to say "I don't know", or "They never really thought it would come to this". The child might even ask if things were ever like this, looking at some forgotten picture book. If there were enough wood to make picture books.

Fantasy books, my favourite kind, almost always have another world in them. Why? So many wonderful books are filled with tales of dense forests, rainforests included. Are we not pleased with the world we live in? Of course not. Why should we be pleased with a world filled with pollution, and terrible things happening that scroll across our conscience when ever we have spare time? I love to write fantasies, and the worlds I place inside are never some kind of high-tech, modern world. I know friends who, given the choice, would love to talk about all of the "cool" inventions that are to come with the future. However, it makes me shudder to think that most of these will be a futile attempt to keep humanity alive and well.

I know every one has the right to say they are proud of who they are. I cannot see any reason to argue with that. What I am asking is if you are pleased with the acts of humanity as a whole.

I know that there are always those who will say what we are doing is right. I know that my point of view may be "immature" and that I am not currently doing anything myself to help anyone.

The truth is I very simply can not.

The truth is you could.

I know several people will be laughing like they hardly ever do right now, saying that I myself am using up the precious rainforest, writing and printing this on paper. However, while doing so, I hope to raise your, and perhaps many others awareness, of all the things we are doing, and that they can help. I can only hope my "immature" opinion counts for going somewhere other than in one ear, out the other. If it has, I do not necessarily mean you have to go marching up to some place and wave signs around. You could just tell more people, or talk about it with a friend. Maybe you could even give a small donation, or even a large one, to help an endangered species, or the rainforest, or others like you…and by doing so, help yourself. It is your choice, and I hope that I have helped by writing this. This is all I can do.

The rest is up to you.

Olivia Williams, Grade 5 Student

ᐃᓛᓐᓂᒃᑯ ᐃᑯᓪᓚᒃᑳᑦᑕᕋᓚ ᖃᓄᐃᓪᓚ
ᐱᑕᕐᕆᐊᒃᓴᖅᑲᖅᑲᑕᒪᓕᖅᑰᑦ, ᐊᕐᕌᒍᓐᖏᑦᑐᓂ.
ᐃᑯᓪᓚᒃᑲᑦᑕᓯᒪᓂ ᑕᐃᒪᓐᓇ? ᖃᓄᐃᓪᓚ ᑐᖁᑦᑎᖅᑲᑦ
ᒪᖔᑦᑕ, ᖃᓄᐃᓪᓚ ᐅᓇ ᑕᓯᕆᐊᖅᑳᑦᑕᒪᖔᑦᑕ,
ᖃᓄᐃᓪᓚ ᐅᖓ ᑕᖅᑳᑦᑕᖅᒪᖔᑦᑕ ᑐᓵᑦᑐᑎᖅᑲᑦᑕᖅᒪᖔᑦᑕ
ᑲᐱᒪᕿᖅᓱᐊ ᐊᒻᒪ ᐅᖕᐱᖅᓂᖅ ᐱᓪᓗᒍ....

ᑐᖁᑦᑎᓂᖅᒥᑦ ᐅᖅᑲᐅᓯᖅᑳᖅᑲᓚ, ᖄᐅᔾᒪᓯᖕᒐ
ᐃᑯᓪᓚᖅᑲᑦᑕᖅᑐᒃᓴᐅᓯᓯ, ᖁᕿᐅᑎᓂ, ᓴᓂᖕᓂ
ᐊᒻᒪ ᖁᓂ ᐊᓐᖏᕐᕆᑐᐊᓗᓃ ᓯᑯᖓ ᑎᑭᐅᑎᓪᓚ-
ᑎᒃᑯᓂ ᐱᕋᔭᖕᓂᖅᑐᑦ. ᐊᒻᒪ ᐊᔾᔨᖕᒥ
ᐃᑯᓪᓕᔪᒃᓴᑎᓴᑎ ᓂᓪᓚᓐᓇᖅᑐᐊᓗᐃ, ᑎᒥᒥᓂ-
ᐊᓗᐃ.... ᐅᐊᑦᑎᐊᕈ ᐊᐃ; ᑭᑯ ᑎᒥᒥᓂᖕᒥᑦ?
ᐃᓄᒥᓂ, ᓂᖅᔪᑎᒥᓂ, ᐅᑯᓂ ᐱᕈᖅᓯᐊᖑᓂ?
ᑕᒡᕙᓂ ᓄᖅᑲᑦᑐᓗ. ᓇᑲᑎᓚᓂᖅ ᐱᕈᔭᐊᓂ
ᓄ ᐸᖅᑐᓂ ᐱᕋᔭᓐᓂ ᐅᓇᐅᖅᓱ ᓚᖕᒋᐅᓃᖅ ᐊᐃ?
ᑭᓇ ᑕᒃᑯᓂᖕᒪ ᐃᒃᐱᒍᓱᒃᑲᔭᖅᐸ? ᑕᒪᒃᑯᓂᖕᒪ
ᐊᒥᓱᓂ ᐃᓱᑲᔭᖅᐸ ᑭᓇ? ᐊᒥᓱᓂ ᐱᖅᑲᖅᑐᒍ.
ᖃᓄᖅ ᐊᑯᓂᐅᐃᐅᑲᔭᖅᐸ? ᐃᓪᓕᖅᑲ ᐊᖅᑯ
ᖁᓕ ᐅᖕᒪᑕ ᓄᖕᖑᓂ. ᖃᔾᔪᐸ ᓇᕐᖁᐃ
ᓄᑲᑎᖅᑕᐅᖅᑲᐅᐸ ᓚᓇᓴᖅ? ᐊᒥᖁᑲᔪᓗᐃ.
ᓱᖁᒪᖕᒍᐊᑐᐃᓐᓇᖕᒥᖕᒍᖕᒪ, ᑕᒪᒃᑯ ᖁᓗᔪ ᐊᒥᖁᐸ
ᐃᓅᑉ ᐊᓐᓂᑕᐅᓯᒪᖁᑦ.

ᐅᓪᓗ ᐃᒃᓵᓐᖏᓐᓂᖅᑐᑦ ᐃᖅᑲᓈᔭᖅᑐᑦ ᐅᓪᓗᕐᒥᒃ
ᐱᖑᐊᖅᑎᓐᓂᖅᑐᑦ ᖃᓄᖅᐳᐊᓗᒃᑐᑦ, ᑖᕐᓇᔭᖅᑐᑦ ᑕᓗᓐᓂᒃ,
ᔨᕆᔪᑦ, ᐳᓂᒃᔪᑦ ᐊᓯᖏᓪᓕᑐᑎᒍ ᐃᓄᐃ
ᐅᖅᑳᓚᐅᕐᒪᑦ. ᒪᑐᐃᖅᑎᕐᓂᖅᑐᑦ ᐅᓛᑦᑎᓐᓂ, ᖃᐅᔨᒪᔪ-
ᐊᓲᑦ ᐃᓕᖅᑲ ᖃᐅᑖᒪ ᑕᐃᒪᓐᓇ ᐃᓅᒍᑦ
ᖃᐅᑕᒫᓂᒃᑎᑎᒋ ᐊᑐᖅᑐᑎᒍ, ᐅᓛᑦᑎᓐᓂ
ᐅᐱᒋᓪᓚᖅᒋᑦ ᐊᑑᑎᖃᓚᐅᕐᒥᓂᑦᑎᓐᓂ ᐳᖅᑯᒍᑦ.
ᐳᓛᑦᑎᓐᓂ ᐅᖃᐅᓯᖃᓪᓚᒃᒋᑦ ᓱᓛᑭᐊᖅ, (3) ᐃᑯᓪᓗᑎ-
~~ᖃᓂᑦ~~ (2) ᑕᒪᒃᑯᓂᖕᒋᓯᑲᕈᓐ ~~ᓂ~~ ~~ᐱᐊ~~ (1) ᓈᓚᒃᑐᓂᒃ
ᐅᖁᔨᔭᐊᒥ ᓈᓚᒃᑐᓄ ᐱᕈᖅᓴᐃᕗᓯᒪᔪᑦ
ᓇᓪᓖᕐᕕᒋᓪᓚᕆᐊ? ᐃᓕᓐᓂ ᐊᓕᓴᖅᑐᒍᓗᐃ
ᓴᒪᑐᒥᐅᑲ ᑐᓴᕐᑎ, ᐃᑦᓚᒐᔭᖅᑐᐃ ᓂᖅᔪᑎᓂ
ᐃᒪᖅᔪᒥᐅᑕᐃ, ᐱᕈᔪᐊᖅᓯᔭᐊᓂᓪᓗᑦ ᖃᓄᓗ.
ᐊᕐᓱᖅᑲᓗ ᐅᖅᑲᐅᓯᐅᑦᔪᓕᖅᑲᐅᓪᓗᓂ ᑕᒪᒃᑯᐊ
ᓴᖅᑐᐃ ᓇᑲ ᕿᖅᑕᐅᔭ ᑐᕋᓂᔪᕕᓗᐅᔪᕆ
ᐃᓪᓗᓯᐅᕙᓗ, ᐃᓪᓗᓯᐅᕙᐃ ᓂᖅᑭᓴᓗᐊᒍᑐᐊᓂᖅ-
ᐊᖅᑎᑐᑎ ᓂᕆᕕᖕᓂ? ᐅᓪᓗ ᐃᓐᖏᑎᒍ
ᐊᐅᓚᑦᑎᕈᐳᔪ, ᐄᓕᓵᖅᑎᖃᕐᓯᔭᕐᒥᓚᒍ ᑕᒪᒃᑯᓂᖕᒐ
ᕿᔪᓂᖅᓴᓂ. ~~ᖃᐅᔨᒪᓂᖅᑲ~~
ᓱᑭᖅᑲᑎᒥᓪᓗᑦ ᑐᓴᖅᑕᐅᓇᔪᒃᑯᑦ, ᐅᖅᑲᓪᓗᑕ
ᓵᒪᕐᒥᑦᑐᓕᐅᒪ, ᐃᒃᐱᒍᓱᑦᑎᐊᕈᓇ ᑕᖅᑯᒥᖕᒐ
ᖁᔭᓇ ~~ᐅᐅᐅ~~ ᐃᒪᖅᔪ ᔪᐊ ᓇᔾᔭᖅᑲᖅᓂᖕᒐ,
ᑲᓇᐃᓕᒪ ᓴ ᓇᐃᓗᕈᑎᒥᖕᑎᐸᑎᒃ?

ᓂᕐᔪᑎᑦᓯ ᓚᐃ ᓇᓄᕐᕋᕐᐳᖅ ᐅᕐᑯᓯᕐᓯᐊᕐᒥᒃ ᐱᓂᕐᕈᐊᕐᕕᖕᒥ
ᐃᒪᕐᔪᐅᓯᒥ, ᐅᕆᐊᓗ ᐊᕐᑭᕐᕋᓇᓯᕐᒥ ᓱᕋᕐᑎᕐᐸᓂᐊᕐᓗᑎᒍ.
ᐃᓕᖅ, ᐃᖕᓇᐅᓕᓇᕐᑭᕐᓗᒐᓗᐊᖅ, ᑭᓯᐊᓂᕐᑕᐅᖅ
ᐃᑲᔪᕐᓱᕐᑎᕐᒥᒐᓐᓂᑦ ᑕᒪᒃᑯᐊ ᓄᓇ ᐃᕐᑎᕐᑲᐊᕆᐊ, ᐊᒃᓱᕐᓗᓂ ᑭᓴᓇᕐᑲᕐᑕᕐᑭᒃ
ᑲᓇᐃᓴᐅᕐᑲᕐᑕᕐᑭᕐᔪᓐᓂ), ᐃᓂᕐᓄᑦ ᐃᑲᔫᑎᕐᑲᕐᓴᕐᑭᕐᒪᕐ (ᐊᒃᓗᑎᒍᓯᕐᑭᕐ
ᐊᒃᓗᑎᒍᓴᕐᐅ ᐊᔫᕐᓄ ᔪᕗᕆᖕ ᓂᕐ ᔪᕗᓂᕐᑎᖕᓂ, (ᔪᕗᕆᖕ)
ᓄᑦᕐᑲᕐᑯᓗᐃ ᐊᐱᓚᒍᓴᕿᑎ ᐊᕐᓗᓱᕐᑲᒥᓄ ᖃᓄᐃᓪ
ᐃᑲᔪᑕᐅᕐᒥᑕᓯ, ᑕᑯᓱᕐ ᕐᔪᕐᓗᕐᒥ ᐱᐅᓴᕐᓗᕐᒥ.
ᐊᕐᓗᓱᕐᑲᑎᓴᐅᑯ ᑭᐅᓗᐃᕐᓄᕐᑲᓴᕐᔭ "ᐋᒪᐃ". ᐅᕆᐊᓗᕐᓂ
"ᐃᑯᒪᒋᓴᐅᕐᒋᕐᓄᒃᑯ ᑕᐃᒪᐃᓕᕐᓴᕐᓴᒪᕐᓕ. ᓄᑦᕐᑯᓗᕐᒥ
ᐊᐱᓚᓱᕐᑲᕐᑲᓴᕐᔪᖅ ᐅᕐᑯᓱᕐᑦᑐᑕᐃ ᐃᒪᕐᔪᐊᒥ ᓇᓴᕐᓗᐃ
ᐃᒪᐃᑕᐅᕐᒪᕐᓕ, ᕐᑭᒥᕐᑭᐊᕐᔪᓴᕐᓗᑎ ᐊᕐᑭ ᕐᔪᑎᕐᑲᕐᓗᓂ
ᑭᒥᕐᑭᐊᕐᓂ. ᕐᑭᓯᐃ ᐊᒥᓪᓕᕆᓗᐊᕐᓴᑎ ᕐᑭᒥᕐᑭᐊᓕᓴᐊᒃᓴ.

ᑎᑎᕋᓴᐊᖅ ᐃᑯᒪᕐᔭᕐᓂ ᔪᓇᐊᕆᓪᓗᒍ, ᐊᒻᒪ ᑕᒪᒃᑯᐊ
ᓄᓯᒃᑲ ᑕᒪᒃᑯᐊ ᐃᓗᐊᓂ ᐱᒻᒪᕆ ᐊᓗᕐ ᔪᕐᓂᕐᓯᑎ
ᒪᓄᐅᕐᒥ ᓄᓇᒥ. ᐱᕐᑲᓄᓴᕐᑲᐅᕐᑎᓪ, ᐅᕐᑲᐅᔪᕐᑲᕐ-
ᓴᕐᓯᑎ ᑕᒪᒃᑯᐊ ᓗᑦ ᔾᕐᑭᓗᓴᕐᑐᓂ ᔪᕗᓂᕐᑎᖕᓂ.
ᐃᓕᕆᓂ ᐃᑯᒍᕐᑲᐃᕐᓯᓪ ᐅᕆᓂ ᓚᑐᑎᓴᓇᐊᕐᑲᕐ
ᕐᑲᐅᕐᔪᒪᓗᑎ ᑕᒪᒃᑯᐊ ᔾᕐᑭᕐᓴᓴᐊᓗᑎ ᓱᕆᓗᑭᐊᕐᔪᕐᓕᑕ
ᐃ ᓄᕐᓄ ᐃᑲᔫᑎᕐᓱᑎᐅᑲᓄᐊᕐᒪᕐᓕ. ᐊᒥᓯᐊᓗᓚᐃ ᕐᑭᔪᐊᒐᐃ
ᓯᓂᔭᐅᔪᒪᓱᕐ ᓇᓴᕐᑐᒐᓯᓂᕐᒐᕐᑐᓂ. ᕐᑲᓄᐃᓪᒪ?
ᕐᔪᓇᐊᕆᕐᒐᕐᓇᕐᑎᔫ ᑕᒪᓐᓇ ᓄᓈ? ᐊᒃᑲᐅᒐᓗᐊ.
ᑲᓄᐃᓪ ᕐᔪᓇᐊᕐᔪᒃᑲᔭᕐᐱᑕ ᑖᓂ ᓄᓇᒥᓂᕐᓗᑕ
ᕐᑲᓄᐃᕿᓕᔭᕐᑐᐊᓗᓂᓴᓗᒥ?
ᕐᑲᐅᔾᔨᒪᔪᕐᒐ ᑭᓄᐃᓇᕐᒃ ᐃᓯᓂ ᐅᑎᕐᓗᑎ
ᐸᕐᑲᕇᕐᑐᕐ ᑕᑯᓇᕐᒥᕐᑐᕐᒐ ᓇᓪᓕᕐᒥᕐᑎᓇᐊᕐᓯ ᑕᒪᓐᓇ
ᑕᒪᓐᓇ ᐊᐱᕐᔪᑎᕆᓄᑦᑕᕐᑲ ᐃᓄᐃ ᐱᓗᕆ ᒫᓐᓇ.
ᕐᑲᐅᔾᔨᒪᔪᕐᒐ ᐃᓕᕐᑎᑦ ᐅᕐᑲᕐᔪᒪᕐᓚᒐᑦ ᑕᒪᒃᑯᐊ
ᓚᓴᕐᑐᐃ ᓇᑲᑎᑦᑕᐅᓯᓂ ᐊᕐᑲᕐᒪᑦ. ᕐᑲᐅᔾᔨᒪᔪᕐᒐ
ᔾᔪᒪᕆᓴᑲ ᓇᓪᓕᕐᒥᕐᑐᐃᓂᕆᓴᑦ ᐊᒻᒪ ᕐᑲᐅᔾᔨᒪᔪᕐᒐ
ᕐᑲᓄᑭᐊᑕᐅᕐᒥᓈᓪ ᐃᑲᔪᕐᑯᕐᒍᕐᒐ.

ᓴᓇᙳᐊᖅᑲ ᐃᑲᔪᕈᓐᓇᕐᒥᑦᑎᐊᓗᓐᓇᑉᐸᒪ.
ᓴᓇᙳᐊᖅᑲ, ᐃᓅᓯ ᐃᓐᓄᓱᑎ ᐃᑲᔪᕈᓐᓇᖃᑎ.

ᖃᐅᔨᒪᔪᖓ ᐊᒥᓱᐃ ᐃᓕᓐᓇᖏᑦᑐ; ᐅᕙᖓ
ᒧᑦᑐᒥ ᐊᑐᕐᓗᖓ ᑕᒪᑐᒥᖓ ᑎᑎᕋᕐᑐᖓ
ᐃᐸᒍ. ᐃᓯᒪᕙ ᑕᒪᓐᓇ ᑐᓴᖃᐅᕐᓇᓱᒐᕐᑕᕋ
14 ᐃᑉᐱᒍᓴᓇᕐᐸᓐᓇᕋᓱᕐᑐᒍ ᐃᑲᔪᕆᒪᓂᕐᑕᕐᓗᒍ.
ᑐᑎᖃᓂ ᓯᕿᑎᓂ ᓴᓇᐊᑐᕐᑎᕐᑐᕐ. ᐃᓄᖕᓄ ᐅᖅᑲᑕᓗᑎ
ᐃᑐᒪᕆᔭᕐᔪᓂ ᐅᖅᑲᖅᑲᑎᕐᑲᓗᑎ. ᐃᓯᒃ
ᐅᖃᕐᒥ ᑐᓂᔪᐊᖅᑐᑎ ᐊᒥᓱᒥᓗᓂ. ᐃᑲᔪᕐᑎᒥ
ᑕᐳᓂ, ᐃᑲᔪᑐᐃᑲᓇᓯᕈᑎ. ᐃᑐᒪᓯᕐᑐᑎ
ᐃᒪᑐ ᐃᑲᔪᑐᐃᓐᓇᖅᑲ ᑕᒪᓐᓇ ᑎᑎᕋᕐᖃ
ᑕᐃᒪᙵᑐᐊ ᐃᑲᔪᕆᙵᕐᓚ
ᐊᔨᐊ ᐃᓐᓂᑭᔪᐊᓂ

Language: Inuktituk
Translated by: Kim Kangok

Hawthorne *Writes*
because everyone has a story...

YOUR FUTURE IS NOW

14.   Italian – Italiano

Italian is spoken by 61 million people around the world. Italian is mostly spoken in Italy but can also be found spoken in Canada, Brazil, Germany, France and United Kingdom.

My Family

I have a little brother who is three years old. We always plays out-side with our friends in our humongous back yard. I have two big dogs, two kitty cats and one hamster. My favourite foods are peanut butter and jelly sandwiches, banana splits and cauliflower. I enjoy helping my parents clean up around the house such as tidying up the living room and sweeping. I am Canadian, half Italian and Irish.

Alexa Lauzon-Saumure, Kindergarten Student

Ma Famille

Ho un fratellino di tre anni. Giochiamo sempre con i nostri amici nel nostro giardino grandissimo. Ho due cani grandi, due gatti e un criceto. Le cose da mangiare che mi piacciono di più sono il pane con il burro di noccioline e la marmellata, il gelato "banana split" e il cavolfiore. Mi piace aiutare I miei genitori a fare i lavori di casa, come mettere a posto il salotto e scopare il pavimento. Sono canadese e mezza italiana.

Language : Italian
Translated by : Carla Valle Painter

My Grandmother

My earliest memory of my maternal grandmother is a picture in my mind of her standing beside a huge old-fashioned stove in simple farmhouse kitchen, a faded apron speckled with flour tied around her waist, and a wooden spoon in her hand. She always seemed to be cooking something wonderful and the old wooden table, covered with its smooth oil cloth whose pattern had long since been worn away by countless hand washings, was the centre of all the action in her house. As children, we would clamour onto the bench and lean over the table, our mouths watering in anticipation and our eyes focussed on the steaming pots and pans being lovingly tended by her hands. And we would listen to the stories of her life; sometimes she would tell them herself in her halting, soft voice, but sometimes it was one of my aunts or uncles laughingly sharing the nuggets of their lives as they grew up in that house.

She was born in a small village in Italy and journeyed to the United States when she was only nine or ten. By thirteen, she was married to my grandfather, a much older man in his early thirties. As I grew older into my teen years, it seemed unbelievable for her to be married and having children at such a young age when my own life revolved around my friends, music and school. But "that's the way it was done back then" would be the only response to my insistent questions. And thus she began her life in the tiny town of Slippery Rock, Pennsylvania, a coal-mining town with one general store, a gas station with one pump and a church.

My grandparents were very poor right from the start and life was difficult. My grandfather worked long, hard hours in the coal mine, coming home tired and dirty at night just to do it again the next day. My grandmother would cook and clean, tend to the pigs, cows and chickens, and weed the acre of garden in the back of the house. They took in boarders to make ends meet. And my grandmother began to have children.

She had 22 children over the course of her married life, although seven of those children died either at childbirth or shortly after. To keep her family going, every day she would get up with the crow of the roosters and begin the daily task of baking ten loaves of bread, feeding each loaf into the wood-burning oven out back with the long wooden paddle and carefully tending the fire to ensure they wouldn't burn.

It is hard to think of my grandmother without a sense of wonder at the courage and stamina she possessed to face those hardships while still remaining the smiling and gentle woman that she was. It is that courage and inner strength that inspired my own mother, and continues to inspire me and my children to this day.

Francesse Kopczewski, Principal

Hawthorne *Writes*

because everyone has a story...

YOUR FUTURE IS NOW

15. Japanese – 日本語

Japanese

Japanese is spoken by an estimated 122 million people in the world. Over 121 million people live in Japan where it is spoken as a first language. Another estimated million people speak Japanese as a second language and live in countries as far away as Australia, Belize, Canada, Mexico, and the United States.

There are three different writing systems in Japanese: Hiragana, Katakana, and Kanji. Hiragana is the simplest form of written Japanese. There are 46 letters and every Japanese word can be written in Hiragana. Katakana has the same sounds found in Hiragana. While Hiragana is used to write Japanese words, Katakana is used to write words borrowed from other languages (i.e. Milk). Kanji characters are borrowed and simplified Chinese symbols. Each Kanji character represents one or several words. Japanese can be written either horizontally or vertically.

日本語

日本語は世界中で、推定一億二千二百万人の人々に話されている。第一言語として日本語が話されている日本には、一億二千百万人以上の人々が住んでいる。他の、推定百万人の人々は、第二言語として日本語を話し、オーストラリア、ベリーズ、カナダ、メキシコ、合衆国のような遠く離れた国々に住んでいる。

日本語には三種類の異なる書き方がある。ひらがな、カタカナ、漢字である。ひらがなは日本語の書き言葉の中で一番単純な形態である。４６の文字があり、日本語の全ての言葉は、ひらがなで書くことが出来る。カタカナとひらがなは同じ音声を表現する。ひらがなは日本語の言葉を書くのに使われるのに対して、カタカナは外来語を書くのに使われる。（例：ミルク）漢字は中国の字を借用し、単純化された。各漢字は一個又は数個の言葉を現す。日本語は横に、又は縦に書くことが出来る。

Language Description by: Yukie and Mike Fuchigami
Translation by: Yukie Fuchigami

My Stamp Collection

I have an awesome stamp collection. In my stamp collection there are lots of stamps from Israel. I also have a Canadian stamp about 100 years old. One of my favorite stamps is the Chinese year of the snake. I enjoy collecting stamps.

In my stamp collection I have a starter kit. My mom and dad gave me this starter kit for my ninth birthday. I this starter kit, there are a pair of tongs, some stamps in mint condition, a large magnifying glass, a binder to hold my stamp collection, a small book that tells you about stamp collecting, and a special sheet that has small plastic pockets to keep your stamps safe. I really enjoy my starter kit.

I sometimes get stamps from my parents and grandparents. My parents sometimes save stamps from the mail. I like it when I relatives from a different country mail us because then I get stamps from that country. My grandma and grandpa on my mom's side also save stamps for me and sometimes go to the post office to get stamps for me. My parents and grandparents sometimes give me stamps.

I started collecting stamps not to long ago. I only started to collect stamps two years ago. My grandma and grandpa on my mom's side last summer gave me some little packages with a series of small stamps in them. One of my first Canadian stamps were the golf championship in 2004. I started my collection only a couple years ago. I really like my stamp collection. One of the reasons I like my collection is because it is fun and exciting. Another reason is that it is a bit of an adventure because you never know what stamps you might run into. I also like stamps because there are stamps on almost every subject so you can most likely get at least one stamp on that subject. My stamp collection is amazing.

Daniel Mayer, Grade 3 Student

僕の切手収集

僕はものすごい切手収集を持っている。僕の切手収集の中には、沢山のイスラエルからの切手がある。僕は又、約１００年の古さの、一枚のカナダの切手を持っている。僕が好きな切手の一つは、中国の巳年の切手だ。僕は切手を集めるのが楽しみだ。

僕の切手収集の中には、初心者用の一式がある。僕のお父さんとお母さんが、この初心者用の一式を、僕の９歳の誕生日にくれた。この初心者用の一式の中には、一組のピンセット、真新しい数枚の切手、大きな虫眼鏡、僕の切手収集をしまっておくバインダー、切手収集について説明した小冊子、そして、小さなプラスチックのポケット付きの、切手を安全に保存する為の特別なシートが入っている。僕は本当にこの初心者用の一式を楽しんでいる。

僕は時々、両親と祖父母から切手をもらう。僕の両親は、時々郵便物の中から切手を取っておいてくれる。その国の切手が得られると言う理由で、僕は異国の親戚から郵便を受け取るのが好きだ。僕の母方の祖父母も、僕の為に切手を取っておいてくれるし、時々、僕の為に、郵便局へ切手を買いに行ってくれる。僕の両親と祖父母は、時々僕に切手をくれる。

僕は少し前に切手の収集を始めた。僕は、ほんの二年前に切手の収集を始めたのだ。僕の母方の祖父と祖母は、去年の夏、僕に、小さな切手のシリーズの入っている小さな包みをくれた。僕の最初のカナダの切手の一つは、２００４年のゴルフチャンピオンの切手だった。僕は、ほんの数年前に収集を始めた。

僕は本当に切手収集が好きだ。僕が収集が好きな理由の一つは、面白くてワクワクするからだ。他の理由は、どんな切手に出会うか想像も出来ないので、少々冒険的だからだ。ほとんど全ての主題の切手があるので、その主題の切手を、多分、最低一枚は得られるはずだから、僕は切手がすきなのだ。僕の切手収集は驚くばかりの収集である。

Language: Japanese
Translated by: Yukie Fuchigami

Passion

Sometimes, it starts with a single idea. .

For me, it all started in Africa. I was swimming in a sea of children playing at sport health festivals across Zambia. Parents, family members and community leaders laughed as they lead the children through various games. The stadium was bursting as more children flooded in. Then, the clouds broke and he stepped in. He was the national football hero in a land where football was more precious than water. He was their Wayne Gretsky, David Beckham and Michael Jordan all rolled into one. Kalusha Bwalya had arrived and the crowd exploded.

In 2003, I found myself working in Zambia for a Canadian organization called Right To Play. As part of an international team, we worked beside local Zambians to implement health education through sports and play programs. Working with UNICEF, the Right To Play headquarters in Toronto, government health officials and several local Zambia organizations, we mobilized over 600 adult volunteers and 14,000 children to get vaccinated against Measles at five simultaneous festivals. The highlight for many was the appearance of several local, national and Olympic level Zambian athletes who supported the campaign. Working for Right To Play was an empowering experience for me. I witnessed how passion and dreams can become reality.

Dual-track books are stories that are written in two different languages. I first heard about dual-track books from a fellow teacher. Renee and I were both taking an online course about teaching English as a Second Language offered by the University of Toronto (OISE/UT.)

"I use it in my classroom," wrote Renee. "We write stories in English and at the end, we match the child with a parent volunteer to help translate the English text into another language."

Wow. Thinking back to the children cheering in Zambia, I wondered: What if we wrote a dual-track book? Not just one class, but the entire school? Based on my experiences from Zambia, I knew how large scale events can bring satisfaction to those involved and inspire others to act. What better way to show students the importance of the writing process, than to give them the thrill of seeing their words in a book? What better way to celebrate diversity in the classroom than by embedding other languages and cultures into our curriculum?

I shared my idea with Susan, a colleague at Hawthorne. She showed me her multi-language classroom and then directed me towards Thornwood, a school in Mississauga, Canada who had run a similar dual-language project and showcased their work online. It all clicked into place. I felt like shouting from the mountaintops but I started smaller by quietly asking a few teachers what they thought. Would it work? How could we do it? The idea was germinating.

Armed with some grassroots support, I approached our principal. Francesse has been enthusiastic about Hawthorne Writes since the beginning. Through some good discussions, we shared ideas to make sure our project could grow within our school board's guidelines. In December, 2005, I presented the dual-track concept at our regular staff meeting: Hawthorne Writes was received with applause and excitement.

The idea was growing by leaps and bounds, but nothing had appeared outside on the surface yet. Susan and I worked hard to encourage the roots of our project to grow. Armed with Arabic and Somali translators, we presented Hawthorne Writes to the parents of different communities. We met with the parents at our school council.

On March 20, 2006, our idea broke the surface of the ground. We held school assemblies where we shared our vision with the students. Armed with guest speakers and stories about family treasures, the students of Hawthorne started to catch the fever. When are we writing our stories? Are we really going to make a book? It's going to be online? The school was hooked and the rest is history. You're holding the product of passion in your hands right now.

Michael Fuchigami, Grade 8 / ESL Teacher

情熱

時にそれは、ほんの思い付きから始まる・・・

私の場合、それは全てアフリカで始まった。ザンビア中で開催された、保健体育のフェスティバルで遊ぶ子供達の海の中を、私は泳いでいた。親達、家族の面々、地域社会のリーダー達は、色々なゲームを通して、子供達を導きながら笑っていた。競技場は更に多くの子供たちが押し寄せた為、溢れていた。その時、雲がちぎれて、彼が足を踏み入れた。彼は、水よりもフットボールの方がはるかに貴重である土地の、フットボールの国民的英雄であった。彼は、彼らのウエイン グレツキー、デイビッド ベッカム、マイクル ジョーダンを全て集めて一つにしたようなものであった。カルシャ バリャが到着し、群衆は爆発したのだった。

２００３年、私はザンビアで、「ライト トゥー プレー（遊ぶ権利）」と呼ばれるカナダの団体で働くことになった。国際チームの一員として、私達は現地のザンビア人のそばで、運動や遊びのプログラムを通して、保健教育を果たす為に働いた。ユニセフ、「ライト トゥー プレー」トロント本部、政府の保健職員、幾つかのザンビアの現地団体と協力して、私達は5箇所の同時フェスティバルにおいて、麻疹の予防接種を受けさせる為に、６００人以上の成人希望者と１４，０００人以上の子供達を動員した。一番の呼び物は、このキャンペーンを支持する、数人の、地域の、全国規模の、そしてオリンピックレベルのザンビアの運動選手が来てくれたことだった。「ライト トゥープレー」で働くことは、私にとって力を与えられる経験であった。私は、情熱と夢が、いかにして現実になるかを目撃したのだ。

二重言語書籍は、二つの異なる言語によって書かれた物語である。私は同僚の教師から、初めて二重言語書籍なるものについて聞いた。レネーと私は二人共、トロント大学 ((OISE/UT)のオンラインコースで、第二言語としての英語の教授法のコースを取っていた。

「私はそれを授業に使っているのよ」と、レネーは書いて来た。「私達が英語で物語を書き、最後に、子供を、英語の原文を他の言語に翻訳してくれる親のボランティアと組み合わせるのよ」

すごい！ザンビアで子供達が喝采するさまを思い起こしながら、私は思ったのだ。「私達が二重言語の本を書いたらどうだろうか？」と。一学級だけではなく、全校で書いたらどうだろうか？ザンビアでの経験から、私は、大規模なイベントが、いかに、それに関わった人々に満足感をも

たらすか、そして、いかに他の人々に行動することを鼓舞するかを知っていた。生徒達に書き方の手順の重要性を示す為には、一冊の本の中に自分達の言葉を見てワクワクさせること以上に良い方法があるだろうか？学級の多様性を謳歌する為には、私達の指導要綱の中に、他の言語と文化を埋め込むこと以上に良い方法があるだろうか？

私は自分の思い付きをホーソーンの同僚であるスーザンに話した。彼女は私に、彼女の多言語学級を見せてくれた。そして、カナダのミシサガ市の学校で、類似した二重言語のプロジェクトを実施し、彼らの成果をインターネット上に展示しているソーンウッドへと導いてくれた。全てが所定の位置にあてはまったのだ。私は山頂から叫びたいような気持ちではあったが、二、三人の教師達にそっと、どう思うかを聞いてみると言うように、ささやかに始めた。成功するだろうか？どんな風に出来るだろうか？その思い付きは発芽していた。

いくらかの草の根的な支援の準備をして、私は校長に相談した。フランセスは初めからホーソーン　ライツ（ホーソーンが書く）について、大変熱心であった。大変有意義な討論を経て、私達の企画が教育委員会のガイドラインに添って発展出来ることを確認する為に、私達は意見を交換した。２００５年１２月、私はこの二重言語の概念を、私達の定例職員会議に提示した。ホーソーン　ライツは拍手と激励を持って、受け取られた。

その思い付きはとんとん拍子で育ってはいたが、表面にはまだ何も現れてはいなかった。スーザンと私は、私達の企画の根が成長するのを促す為に、一生懸命働いた。アラビア語とソマリ語の翻訳者の準備をして、私達はホーソーン　ライツを異なる地域社会の親達に提示した。私達は学校の評議会で親達と会合した。

２００６年３月２０日、私達の思い付きは地表を破ったのだ。私達は、私達の洞察力を生徒達と共有する為の学校集会を持った。来賓の講演者と家族の宝物の話が準備されて、ホーソーンの生徒達は熱狂的になって行ったのだった。いつ、私達の物語を書くの？私達、本当に本を作るの？オンラインに載るの？学校中が、はまってしまい、後は周知の事である。今、あなたはその手に、情熱の成果を握っている。

Language: Japanese
Translated by: Yukie Fuchigami

Hawthorne *Writes*
because everyone has a story...

16.   Korean –한국어

Korean is spoken by over 67 million people around the world. Most of these people live in South Korea and North Korea. It is also spoken around the world in China, Japan, Russia, Thailand, Germany and Brazil, to name a few countries.

Hangul, The Korean Alphabet

One example of Korea's unique culture is Hangul, the Korean alphabet. There is no record in history of a king who made a writing system for the benefit of the common people except in Korea.

For example, each Chinese character has a meaning, so people have to memorize all of them, but the Korean alphabet is made of phonetic letters just like English. It is easy to learn because it can be put together with 10 vowels and 14 consonants. Hangul has 8,000 different kinds of sound and it is possible to write each sound.

Hangul was invented 500 years ago, but all Koreans have only used it for 100 years. Today it stands in the world proudly with its value. The Korean illiteracy rate is near the zero percent mark, because Hangul is easy and scientific.

한글, 한국의 문자

독특한 한국문화의 하나의 예는 바로 한글이라고 할 수 있다. 한국을 제외하고는 왕이 일반 백성을 위해 문자체계를 만들었다는 역사 기록은 존재하지 않는다.

예를 들어, 중국문자 하나는 하나의 의미를 가지므로 사람들은 모든 중국문자에 대해 기억을 해야 한다. 그러나 한글은 영어와 마찬가지로 같이 음성문자들로 이루어져 있다. 10 개의 모음과 14 개의 자음을 조합하여 약 8,000 개의 서로 다른 소리를 낼 수 있으며, 각 소리를 한글을 이용하여 기록할 수 있으므로 배우기가 매우 쉽다.

한글은 500 년전에 발명이 되었으나 100 년전부터 모든 한국사람들이 사용해왔다. 오늘날 한글은 그것의 가치로 인해 세계에 우뚝 서 있다. 한글은 매우 쉽고 과학적인 문자이기 때문에 한국인의 문맹률은 거의 0 에 가깝다.

Language Description and Translation by: Dongsik Kim and Solbee Kim

Different Religions

My father and mother have completely different religions. My father is Buddhist and my mother is an Atheist.

Atheism is when you believe there is no god and no second life or reincarnation. My mother is also a Humanist; she believes that you should live life ethically, care for others, and be as honest as possible in your dealings with them.

Buddhism is quite different. In Buddhism there is reincarnation, you have many lives and you have to be respectful and kind in each one to get to a higher life form. If you are disrespectful, you might get a life form that is difficult like a small bug, where you have to work hard to survive as punishment. There are also many different "minds" to develop, some of which are love, patience, and happiness. Eventually, once you have lived many lives, expressed many kindnesses and developed all the minds, you become a Buddha. There is also meditation which lets you empty the mind, which my father does on a regular basis.

My mother and father respect each other's religions even though they are different. My grandmother and grandfather on my mother's side used to be Protestant (like my mother); my grandmother was raised a Baptist, and my grandfather was raised in the United Church. Both of them respect my mother's beliefs, but my grandmother really wanted my mum to get married in a church. My mum and dad did some research and decided to get married in a Unitarian Church. The Unitarians have very broad, open ideas about religion that do not violate my parents' religious beliefs. Getting married in a Unitarian church was a good solution, because it pleased my grandmother but it didn't force my parents to express something that they did not believe.

My grandmother on my father's side is Episcopalian (an American religion that is like Anglicanism in Canada). She respects my father's beliefs. My uncle was a Catholic priest (he wasn't allowed to get married) but he decided not to be. Later he married my aunt, who was raised as an Episcopalian, and he became an Episcopalian priest.

When my aunt got older, she began to celebrate nature by marking special times like the Winter Solstice.

I don't think I am Buddhist or Atheist. I believe that there is a god but he/she/it doesn't have that much control over you and you have to make most of your choices. I like to think that better things will happen to you if you make better choices. I also don't really believe in reincarnation or a second life, but I definitely believe there is some kind of god, and if you pray and make good choices then you will have a good life. I think you should always respect other peoples' religions, even if they are different from yours.

Merissa Taylor-Meissner, Grade 5 Student

　나의 아빠와 엄마는 다른 종교를
가지고 있다. 아빠의 종교는 불교이고 엄마의
종교는 아테네이스트(Atheiet)이다. 엄마의
종교는 만약 그 종교를 믿으면 신도 두번째 삶
도 없다. 나의 엄마는 인간이다. 그녀는 그녀 보다
다른 사람을 먼저 생각하고 노력한다고 해야
한다고 믿고 있다. 하지만 불교는 아주 다르다.
불교는 많은 사람에게 예의 있고 친절하게
대하며 각각 높고 낮음의 차이가 있다.
만약 내가 예의 없고 불친절 하거나 하며
내 인생은 벌레 같은 작은 인생을 살 것이다.
어떤 일이 힘들어도 참고 좋은 생각만 하며
살아 가는 것이 불교이다. 명상을 할땐 머리
를 비우고 우리 아빠는 매일 명상을 한다.
우리 부모님은 각각 자신들의 종교를 존경해
준다. 나의 외가 쪽은 엄마의 종교를 믿고
친가 쪽은 아빠의 종교를 믿는다고 생각
하겠지만 모두 다른 종교를 믿는다. 하지만
언제나 서로를 존경해 준다. 심지어는 크리스찬
쪽의 종교는 아니지만 교회에서 결혼을
했었을 정도이다. 나는 내가 불교 이제나
아테네이스트(Atheiet)라고 생각 하진
않는다. 나는 신 이라는 것이 사람의

마음을 존중하거나 모든 길을 신이 차저 하지
않는 다고 믿는다. 나는 사람이 생각하는 대로
하는 것이 더 나은 방법이라고 생각 한다.
또한 나는 할머니, 할아버지 의 종교는 만지
않눈다. 만약 내가 기도를 하면 내 삶이
좋아진다 라는 종교를 믿진 않지만 나는 언제나
다른 종교를 존중 해 주어야 한다고 생각한다.
만약 종교가 다르더라도 말이다.

Language: Korean
Translated by: Sol Bee Kim, Grade 7 Student

My Great Grandmother

On the third day of July 1926, in Westmoreland, Jamaica, my great grandmother was born. She was named, Delores "Mama" Baker. I don't know much about my great grandmother's childhood but a lot is because I never thought to ask her when she was alive. Now that she is gone I regret not asking her more about her life

As an adult Delores was a housewife. She was married to a man named Masli, who died in 1971. This left Delores alone to raise her fifteen children.

Delores also took take care of her grandchildren, some of her great grand children, and some nieces and nephews. Delores's house was always filled with people; it was never empty. People loved to visit Delores because Delores was so kind and sweet. Everyone felt safe and loved when they were with her. She was so trusted that family and friends would often drop their children off to her. Everyone would stop by every day to see Delores and get the town gossip.

As the years passed, Delores's children, grandchildren, great grand children, and nieces and nephews, started to leave Jamaica. Her children moved to Canada. Delores's house started to seem quiet and empty. So Delores' youngest son, Paul, and her daughter, Termuter took Delores with them Canada. It took Delores and her family a while to settle in and be comfortable with their new home.

While Delores lived in Canada she watched her family continue to grow. Delores became a grandmother and a great grandmother, an aunt and a great aunt many times over. Her family was now huge.

Today our family is so big that it is impossible to count everyone. There was only one day that I remember being able to count my family members. The day of my every single member is impossible to count; and is still increasing. But people in our family have died.

While Delores lived in Canada she lived with her youngest son, Paul, his two daughters, and wife. The only time I got to see my great grandmother was on Sunday's at church, or on special occasions. I loved seeing her because she made me feel so happy and loved. Her smile shined like the sun, which just brightened my day. I will always love her.

On the 9th day of March 2002, Delores died. I really don't know how she died, because none of the adults will tell the kids. A couple of days before she died she was in the General Hospital. Family and friends that were in the area came to see Delores at the hospital. Everyone missed worked and school and stayed at the hospital all day. They went home at night but no one could sleep. The next day everyone came to see again. We were all scared that she was going to die and we were worried for her.

A couple of days later, the doctor came and told us that she didn't make it. Delores had died. To this day, I will always hate those words; she didn't make it.

Delores' funeral was held at Calvary Pentecostal Church, on Saturday, March 16, 2002, at 10:00 a.m. The church was so full that people had to stand in the back. All the family members attended, close friends of Delores' came to pay their respects and people who knew her came to say goodbye. She was only 75. She could have lasted longer, but it was her time to go. It took me three weeks to stop crying. Now I realize that I don't need to be so sad because she will always be with me in my heart.

Keleasha Marshall, Grade 7 Student

나의 증조할머니

1926 년 칠월달의 셋 째날 Jamaica 의 Westmoreland 라는 도시에서 나의 증조할머니께서 태어나셨다. 증조할머니께서는 Delores "Mama" Baker 로 이름이 지어졌다. 할머니의 어린시절은 알려지지 않았다. 왜냐하면 나는 할머니에게 물어볼 시간이 많았지만 할머니에게 물어보려고 하면 언제나 시간은 늦어 있었다.

할머니는 어른으로서 가정주부였다. 할머니는 Masil 라는 남자와 결혼했는데 그 남자는 1971 이나 1972 년에 돌아가셨다. 그래서 할머니와 그녀의 열다섯 명의 아이들, 그녀의 중손주, 그녀의 고손주, 그녀의 조카와 조카딸을 남겨 놓았다. 할머니의 집은 언제나 사람들로 꽉 차있었고 결코 비지 않았다. 모든 사람들이 할머니의 집의 방문하길 원했으며 집의 주인인 할머니는 bami 를 구어서 약간의 돈을 벌 수 있었다.

몇 년 전에 할머니의 열다섯 명의 아이들, 증 손주, 고 손주, 조카와 조카딸은 Canada 에서 살기위해 Jamaica 를 떠나게 되었다. 할머니의 집은 할머니의 가장 어린 딸과 아들이 그녀를 Canada 로 모셔드리기 까지 텅텅 비어 있었다. 할머니께서 Canada 에 정착하시고 새로운 집이 편안해질 때까지는 시간이 좀 걸렸다.

시간이 흐름에 따라 할머니의 가족의 수는 점점 늘어났다. 현재는 가족의 수를 셀 수 없을 만큼 커졌고 지금도 늘어나고 있다. 하지만 몇몇 사람들은 돌아가셨다. 할머니는 그녀의 가장 어린 아들과 그의 두 딸, 그의 아들과 그의 아내와 함께 살았다. 유일하게 내가 할머니를 볼 수 있는 날은 일요일 날 교회에서나 특별한 경우에만 가능하였다. 그녀를 보는 것은 내 기분을 좋게 한다. 그녀의 미소는 태양처럼 빛이 났고 그것은 나의 앞날을 밝게 해주었다. 그리고 나는 할머니를 언제나 사랑할 것이다.

하지만 2002 년 3 월 9 일 날 할머니는 돌아가셨다. 나는 할머니가 어떻게 돌아가셨는지 잘 모른다. 왜냐하면 아무도 아이들에게 얘기를 해주지 않았기 때문이다. 할머니가 돌아가시기 몇 일전에 할머니는 종합병원에 입원해 있었다. 가족의 절반이 그녀를 보기위해 각각이 다른 나라에서 왔다. 모든 가족이 일이나 학교를 가지 않고 병원에만 계속 있었고 밤에서 집에 돌아갔다. 하지만 아무도 잠을 잘 수 없었으며 다음 날 그녀를 보러 들르곤 했다. 우리는 무섭고 걱정이 되었다. 그리고 며칠 뒤에 의사가 와서 할머니께서 돌아가셨다고 말했다. 그것은 내의 삶에서 들었던 가장 끔찍한 일이였다.

　　장례식은 2002 년 3 월 16 일 토요일 아침 10 시 Calvary Pentecostal Church 에서 있었다. 교회에는 사람들로 가득 차서 뒷 부분까지 사람들이 서 있었다. 가족 모두와 할머니의 친한 친구들 그리고 할머니를 알고 있는 사람들이 참석했다. 할머니의 연세는 75 세 였다. 할머니는 더 오래 사셨어야 하는데 돌아가실 시간이었다. 할머니의 죽음을 극복하는 데는 3 주정도의 시간이 걸렸으며 할머니는 항상 나의 마음속 깊은 곳이 있기 때문에 장례식때 나는 울지 않았다고 이해하고 있다.

Language: Korean
Translated by: Sol Bee Kim, Grade 7 Student

The Rolling Pin

My story is about a rolling pin that has been passed down from generation to generation in my family. My great-grandmother was the one that bought this cherished rolling pin. She made many pies and pastries, such as meat pies, sugar pies, homemade bread, and many more delicious goodies. I don't think my great-grandmother knew that she was starting such a tradition when she first bought that rolling pin.

There is a pretty funny story that happened when I was younger that involves this rolling pin. My sister Megan and I were having a fight over whose toy was whose. Megan took my toy, I was furious! I went into the kitchen to find the longest possible item I could reach, and of course, the rolling pin was there. I chased Megan around the house with that rolling pin for hours. It wasn't funny then, but now Megan and I laugh at the story.

This rolling pin has been in my family for quite some time now. My great-grandmother had it, and then my grandfather got it because he was the oldest child of the family. My mother was not the oldest of her family, but she got the rolling pin because she did most of the cooking in her family.

I will most likely never get this treasured rolling pin because my older sister will inherit it. It is nice to dream however, that I will eventually get this rolling pin. I wonder how many more delicious pies and pastries this old, family treasure of ours will make.

Thank you Memère!

Erin Davey, Grade 7 Student

롤링 핀

나의 이야기는 우리 가족 대대손손 전해져 내려온 롤링 핀에 관한 것이다. 우리 증조할머니께서는 이 롤링 핀을 처음으로 사신 분이였다. 증조할머니께서는 고기파이, 설탕파이, 집에서 만든 빵, 여러가지 많은 사탕둥과 같은 많은 파이와 패스츄리를 만드셨다. 나는 증조 할머니께서 처음 그 롤링핀을 사셨을 때 그러한 전통을 시작하고 있다는 것을 모르고 있었다고 생각한다.

내가 지금보다 더 어렸을 때 이 롤링핀과 관련하여 일어났던 아주 재미있는 이야기가 있다. 언니 Megan 과 나는 장난감이 서로 누구의 것인가에 대해 싸우고 있었다. 언니가 내 장난감을 가지고 가서 나는 화가 났다! 나는 부엌으로 들어가서 내 손에 닿을 수 있는 가장 긴 물건을 발견했는데 물론 그것은 롤링핀이었다. 나는 언니를 여러시간동안 집주변을 여기저기 쫓아다녔다 그때 그것은 별로 재미있지는 않았지만 지금 언니와 나는 그 이야기를 하면 웃는다. 이 롤링핀은 꽤 오랜시간 동안 우리가족들과 함께 했다.

나의 증조할머니가 그것을 가지고 계셨고 그리고 그 다음엔 나의 할아버지가 가족중에 가장 나이가 많았기 때문에 그것을 가지게 되었다. 나의 어머니는 가족중에서 나이가 가장 많지는 않았지만 집안에서 거의 모든 요리를 담당해왔기 때문에 지금은 어머니가 그 롤링핀을 가지고 계신다.

나는 나의 언니가 그 롤링핀을 물려받을 것이기 때문에 그 보물과 같은 롤링핀을 가지지는 못할 것이다. 그러나 내가 결국은 그 롤링핀을 가지게 될 것이라고 꿈꾸는 것은 즐거운 일이다. 나는 이 오래된 가족의 보물과도 같은 롤링핀으로 얼마나 많은 맛있는 파이와 패스츄리를 만들게 될 것인지 궁금하다.
감사합니다.

Language: Korean
Translated by: Sol Bee Kim, Grade 7 Student

Hawthorne *Writes*
because everyone has a story...

17.   Kurdish – کوردی

Kurdish is spoken by an estimated 2.7 million people in Iraq and 11 million people around the world.

Freedom

Just imagine you and millions of other people running for freedom and safety. That is what happened to my mom and her whole city of Arbil in Iraq.

It was March 10, 1991 when the president, Saddam Hussein announced that no one was aloud outside after 6:00.pm My mom had a horrible feeling that there would be a fighting because in northern Iraq, there were Kurdish soldiers called Peshmerga who fought for freedom. They would travel south to fight Saddam's soldiers.

Near the house in which mom, and her parents lived was where the fighting would start. In front of the house there was a big open field and behind it is an army base where weaponry is kept. By 4:30pm, my mother's family got all their supplies together: clothing, bread, water, blankets, etc. After that, they headed to my mom's aunt's house because it was a safer place. That night, no one could sleep; all they did was to listen to the radio. The announcer on the Peshmerga's radio told the Iraqi people to go out and fight for their freedom. Many people did: young, old men, women, boys and girls. Many died.

The next night, March 11, the fighting stopped and we had freedom. My mom and the rest of the family decided to return home by 2:30 pm. When they returned, they were shocked to see all those dead and injured bodies on the bloody streets. If only the announcer on the radio hadn't encouraged those young people to fight for their freedom.

They were not only shocked to see the corpses but we were also shocked to see the damage done to their house; there were bullet holes in the walls, furniture, windows, clothing, and there was broken glass and wood everywhere. However that was not the worst thing; the looters had done their work too. The looters stole weapons, jewelry, money, etc from many houses, apartments, shops, and banks.

Freedom lasted for 20 days and nights until attacks started from thousands and thousands of helicopters, and soldiers. That night, April 1st 1991, my mom, her siblings and her parents decided to run away.

Her parents had a pick-up truck but it could only hold 3 people inside and 4-5 people at the back. Only the elderly and the very young were able to ride it. Unfortunately, my mom's aunt and her son were left behind. Saddam's soldiers surrounded Arbil, her Aunt and her Son was in Arbil at that time.

The fighting started suddenly, they all fled north. There was no time to help anyone but yourself. My mom's uncle had taught her before to lie down on her belly and cover her head if she heard missiles that were very near. It would give her a better chance to survive. By the end of the first day, they ran for 30 kilometers.

That night those fighting started closing in on the city. They caught my mom's Aunt and took her son. They later let her but not her son. The fighters buried her son alive along with hundreds of others.

The next day, my mom and her family ran another 45km. By the 5th day they had walked 140km, they finally made it to Iran. That's when my mom's dad's brother died. Her father was extremely disheartened. Her dad had had enough of running that he and told everyone that he was going back to Arbil. A couple of days later everyone returned, after learning that the fight was over.... and they had Freedom.

Alan Shamsedin, Grade 7 Student

ئازادی

بێینه‌ به‌رچاوی خۆت ، تۆو زیاتر له‌ دوو ملیۆن
خه‌لك له‌وه‌ی بكۆمه‌ل بكه‌ن له‌ بینای ئازادی
سه‌ربه‌ستی . غه‌ویه‌ به‌ شێك لزتریان مژوه‌نكی
بنارو مژلاتكه‌م ، هه‌ولێر وكوردستان .
له‌ رۆژی ١٠ ئازاری ١٩٩١ به‌یان قه‌ده‌كرنی
هاتوربووكرا له‌ سناركه‌م له‌ دوای ساعه‌ ٦ی "٦ی
كێوداره‌ ترستی ئۆر له‌ ده‌ورو به‌رو خۆشیه‌ك ئۆر
له‌ ئاغایابو . بریارمانا ماكه‌مان به‌ جن به‌یلین ،
یكین بۆ مال بوره‌ چونكه‌ شوێنی ماكه‌مان ئاستكرابو
كه‌ سه‌ ری ئۆری لیبه‌كرێته‌ له‌ به‌ر نزیكی له‌ بلكه‌ی
ئاساینی دارو ده‌سقه‌ی رژتو به‌سی .
به‌یانی رۆژی ١١ی ئازار بور لكه‌ل گرنگ به‌یان وجانگ
مزگه‌وته‌كان ده‌نگی تۆپ وته‌قه‌ی تفه‌نگ دله‌ان
خسته‌ جۆش مژوشی بۆ هه‌وای ئازادی لكاتێكدا
ده‌نگ رادیۆی بێشمه‌رگه‌ لالاچك تر های هاورا شای ده‌ ا
بۆ هه‌له‌ تبرون بۆ سه‌ ردارودسته‌ی رژیم . هه‌رواش
بور كۆمه‌لانی خه‌لك به‌ هه‌سم چین تۆتبرلك وته‌سی
چیابیا هه‌زرشیان ده‌بروه‌ سه‌ ردوژمن وبه‌ جه‌پله‌
ستران ، هه‌ل ه‌له‌ش لالاجك تر ئه‌ماوه‌نی ئازادی
دوگر در . كاواتان هاته‌ دی دوای قوربانیه‌ك
ئۆرو خونی رشتن و به‌ینداربونی هه‌زاران كه‌سی .

- 163 -

دوای نیوه‌روژی ئهو روژه که‌ وابیه‌وه ساڵی هۆسان
بوڵام حاڵی گرانم بۆ نه‌م هه‌موو که‌ پڕولاوه چوانه‌
که لاسه کایان به‌ده‌م رنگاوه که‌ شوو وه ئه‌ور
به دایک رباوکا شیش وتلی گه‌رال و سوریا بوون
به دوای روله کانیان .

له‌لایه‌ی ترێشی ماڵه‌که‌مان شتووتینه‌وای سته‌ رتلی
گوره به دوور دیه‌ریه دیار بوو وه ئه‌ور له کۆڵ و یه‌ڵی
ماڵه‌که‌مان شتووتنی گوله‌ی پتوه دیار بوو
دوای روژ کاوا بوون نرس و ساڵم به سه‌ر سا ریه‌دا
باڵی کته‌شن لپوو بوو وه‌وام بوون سنه رله‌لایه‌ی وه
دوو چه‌روه یه‌ له‌لایه‌ی تر.

دوای ۲ روژ وبان له کار رهه‌وای کازوی بۆ
جاریکی تر دووه‌م به هه‌ز تکی ئه‌ور وه ئه‌ور دربنانه
هه‌ر شش هه‌تا بۆ سه‌ر کوردستان ، ساڵی هۆسان
هه‌ رتله‌ که وه‌شبوون که جاوه‌ری به‌من تا له تواناسان
دابیت بۆ ماوه‌وه له به‌رگی که‌رن بوڵام له هه‌مان
کاشیش! که‌ل ریه‌کی پتوو سته‌تان کامای که‌ ربوو
بۆ کا تلی نه‌گر تو‌شی راکردن پبین وه‌روی دا
لهوه بوبانی !حه شیه‌ن سته‌ه‌ رهه‌ زاران له خه‌لک
سشا ریک به وله وراکردن توانیان هۆسان برگار
بکه‌ین نه‌مه‌شی دیه‌ان دوابه کا وسه‌تی ئه‌ور گه‌وره
دڵ ته‌زین ، سا یه کتڵ بروم له‌گه ژ کا که وه بابه

بەیەک ئەبقەم چونکە ئەوتۆ مۆبیلە کە مانا بۆ بیر و
هیزدان تەرخان کرد ... دانی گرانم بۆرزاکەوەکەوتە
بوردەسی دوژمنی و تانتـستانی بێ سەردرشوتنە
وهيسدان لاوان تريشي ولك نکو لەوکاوەبسا تەوا
بە زیندوتی زریند جیان کران.

براکەم بەدەم راکردنەوە چنی دەگرتم ئەگەر زانی
تۆبێ ... زنکردنەوە ولك فیکەولك لە گوینەوە نزیلك
بوو لەسەر دەم خۆتە برە بەعەرد و گوتگانت
بە دەستە دلفە بۆ ئەوسی تۆزلي خۆمان بیا ترین
بەگۆنری تەوانا چونکە باسە ... تۆ نکی ئۆرسی بوو
کەس نەیدەتوانی بەطانان کەسەوی ئەوسی لان
بقەومایە لەم دەشتەو دەرەبەمن دلما ، وە جەنان
ژیران ... دەبیر بەمۆنا بۆ مباران و سەرمار
صیلاک بورە تۆرباخنە ئەم کۆژەوە.

دەای پنج بنز و کۆژمەکمان کە دیشتە سنوری
عیراق ئیران ، دەای چونە ئاوخای ئیران کوردەکانە
ئەوینا نۆرەجۆگەرەی نتەم و ... خەلك تریان
گرتەخۆ و ... نیان کردین . خاك ئیران بووەشونی
گۆری خامی دای کەوسا لەدەی کۆچی دوایوکرد ... نتەمەشی
دەای نزیکیان دی رۆژ گۆرا ... مشاری خۆمان(هەولێر)
دەای نەوسی نەفتەوە ئەگر تۆمان جاودزی دەکرد و
دەبیاراست ، دەدبارونیانی کازدیان بەجاوەت
خۆمان بینی .

Language: Kurdish
Translated by: Bikhal Ismael

Childhood of My Dad

There is someone who is very close to me, for whom I have much respect. Though I thought I knew almost everything there was to know about this person, I have recently learned a whole lot more about Salah Ya-Ali, my father.

Salah Ya-Ali was born in Kurdistan, Iran. He came from quite a large family; he had four brothers, two sisters, and a mother and father. He was raised in a neighborhood called Shahrabany. Shabhrabany was a good place to live; it was filled with many good and respectful families who took care of each other. Unfortunately however not far from this loving neighborhood however, there was a really bad area that was filled with drug dealers, people who abused drugs and thieves. The good thing was that Salahs parents didn't allow him to go anywhere near this place.

While Salah was raised in a middle class family, he had to work at a really young age because he was the oldest child in his family. Salah was eight years old when he started to work; he worked on a construction site where he had to carry really heavy equipment.

In school he was an extremely smart and well-behaved student. He would never ever get a mark below 85%. Once he did so well in school on a really important test that the teachers put his name in the city newspaper. Although Salah was a good student, the teachers would still beat him. The teachers hit him because the teachers in his school and other schools in Iran would use any excuse to hit their students. Once Salah got hit because he made one small mistake, just because of that one mistake the teacher whipped him ten times with a belt.

In addition to being a good student, he played pretty much every sport. He played basketball, soccer, wrestled, and even swam. At first, he wasn't good at any of them but after he practised and put a lot of effort into his sports he became the best. Salah became captain on every single sports team he tried out for, and got gold medals in ever sport he played. After a few years of playing sports, he was offered a lot of money to coach teams. He went on to coach basketball, soccer, wrestling, and even swimming.

Kareem was the name of Salah's closest friend. They were good friends because they were neighbours, and they practically did everything together. Not only did they go to school together but they also joined the army at the same time and became soldiers.

Unfortunately Salah did witness a war; the war between Iran-Iraq. A lot of his friends were in the war; many of them were badly injured, some even died. During the war two of the most devastating things that Salah experienced was the loss of his best friend and when he himself got shot in the upper part of the back.

Nine years after these injuries, Salah made the decision to move to Canada to give his wife and children a better life and for the children's education. In Canada he was able to get surgery on his back and the bullet was removed. To date this is the story of someone who I love and respect very well, my father Salah Ya-Ali.

Behnam Ya Ali, Grade 7 Student

کاک مندانی باوکم

کەسێك هەیە کەزۆر نزیکە لێم ، کەزۆر رێزم بۆی هەیە ،
من وەرەمزانی کەوا ئەو نۆزانی دەریاوەی ، بەکەم بەم زووانەم
دەستەکردبوو لە ...... بارکە بۆ ..... یاعلی
..... یاعلی لە کوردستان شرانیلمحالیك بووه لە ... باریکی کەورە
بارترتەوەی لایان زەباوچ و چواد بلوتومەرەیەو ... شفاك . استکەوەکی
شهربانی کەورە بوو . شهربانی شوێنێکی باش بوو بۆ ئزلیلانتن
شوێنێکە کەپر لە خیزانی بەرێز وئایاب بووه ئلگاداری
یەکتریان دەکەرد بەداخەسە

..... کەورەترین مندال بوو لەسنرانی لاوخۆشکەکان یان جلەوخوستن
کردبە ئیشکردن لەسەی هەفتەی ساڵی سێشی کردە بەشی
خانوکردن ، جا بێوەریشبوو بەهەلگرتنی شی قورس بوو
لە قوتابخانەدا ئۆتابیکی زۆر نزیرەك بوو بەهیچ شێوەیەك
بلەوبارەی دەدەەمێنا کەمتر لە ٨٥٪ دا جاریك بلەی
زۆربە لای هێنا ئەماوە تاکات ئاوەکەیان ناردبۆ بلاوکردوە
لەلایەوەی رۆژنامەی شار .

وه هه وها صلاح فولايهي قوتابيكي نايلب بوو،
بهلام زۆر چالاك و چالاك بوو له بهشي ومرزهشي.
له هه مه جۆر ومرزهشي پێشگۆت و سهركهوتوو
بوو، لهتوێی سهبهته، وهك فوتبال وه له زۆران باشتر
وه هه روه ها پهلهوار بوو. له پێشنهکردا زۆر باش
نهبوو لهم ومرزهشانه، بهلام له یاریانردا هه ولی
زۆرهدا وهتوانی ببێت به باشترین. وهله یاریاندرا
بوو به سهرۆکی ههمهجۆر وهههمهشیبی ومرزهشی
توانی که نیشانی ئالتوون/زێر بیاتهوه لههه موو
جۆرنه چالاکیێک.

کهریم نزیکترین برادهربوو که زۆر باش بوو بۆ یهکتر
چووبکی دراوسێ بووبن. چوون بۆ قووتابخانه به
پێکهوه و چوون به سهربازی به پێکهوه.
بهداخهوه صلاح چاوی به شهر کهوت، شهری
ئیران و عیراق. زۆربهی برادهرانی بهشدار بوون.
ههندێیان کوژران وههندێیان بریندار بوون.
لهنێوانی شهرهکهدا دووکا رهسات هاته سهر

صەڵح دا. یەکەم باشترین برادەری خۆتا.

وە کارەساتی دووەم لێدرا بە گوللەیەك ، گوللەکە

دای بە ناو شانیدا لە پشتی .

ئەڤین ساڵ لەباتی ئەم برینانە ، صەڵح بریاری دا

کەوا بچێت بۆ کەندا ، لەبەر ئەوەی زیاتی

باشتر ترخان بکا بۆ خزمانەکەی و منداڵەکانی.

وە هەروەها بۆی منداڵەکانی خوێندنیان تەواوبکرێ

لەکەندا یەوانیان گولەكە لابەری بەخەوایت.

تا ئیمڕۆدا ئەمە چیرۆکی کەسێکە کەوا صە

زۆر خۆشم دەوێت وزۆر ڕێزم هەیە بۆی ، جائەم

کەسەش باوکی بەڕێزمە، صەڵح یاعلی .

Language: Kurdish
Translated by: Bikhal Ismael

Hawthorne *Writes*
because everyone has a story...

YOUR FUTURE IS NOW

18.   Portuguese - Português

Portuguese

Portuguese is spoken by an estimated 177 million people around the world. It is the official language of Portugal where 10 million people speak it, however, it is also spoken in Brazil (as the official language), and in Spain, France and several other countries, including Angola, in Africa.

Portuguese uses the Roman alphabet, and is based on Latin. It is similar in structure to Spanish, Italian and French. The Portuguese spoken in Brazil (where some 186 million people live) is very different from that spoken in Portugal.

Português

Mais ou menos 177 milhões de pessoas no mundo falam o português. É a língua oficial do Portugal, onde 10 milliões a falam. É também falado no Brasil (como a língua oficial), e na Espanha, na Fráncia, e em varios outros paises, incluindo a Angola, na África.

A língua portuguêsa usa o alfabeto romano, e se basa no latim. É semelhante, na sua estructura, ao espanhol, italiano e francês. O português que a gente fala no Brasil (com algumas 186 milhões de população) é muito diferente da forma da língua que se fala no Portugal.

Language Description and Translation by: Patricia Saunders

Camping at Uncle Sig's

My favourite family memory is when we camped at uncle Sig's. It was last year. My cousins, aunts, uncles, nana and puba, uncle Sig, auntie Carol came for nana and puba's 50th anniversary. First we packed and then we left for uncle Sig's! He lives in Nova Scotia. Next we set up our tent and we played night time hide and go seek with flash lights. We had a water balloon fight. We had an egg and spoon race. We hunted for jelly fish before we swam. When we woke up there were earwigs in everyone's tent but ours?! We went on a row boat, a paddle boat and a motor boat. Jeff sang with his guitar. We had a BBQ and all the tables were set up under a big tent. We packed up and went home after it was over. It was very fun!

Felipe Bemfica, Grade 1 Student

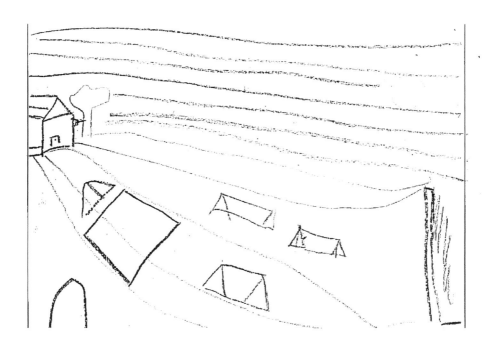

Acampando na casa do tio Sig

Minha recordação favorita de minha família foi quando nós acampamos na casa do tio Sig. Foi no ano passado. Meus primos, tias, tios, nana e puba, tio Sig, titia Carol vieram para o aniversário de 50 anos de casamento da nana e do paba. Primeiro arrumamos as malas e depois saímos para a casa do tio Sig. Ele mora na Nova Escócia. Depois armamos a nossa barraca e brincamos de esconde-esconde no escuro com lanternas. Nós fizemos uma luta com bexiguinhas. Fizemos uma corrida do ovo na colher. Caçamos águas-vivas antes de nadar. Quando acordamos havia lacraias em todas as barracas menos na nossa?! Andamos em um barco a remo, em um pedalinho e em um barco a motor. Jeff cantou com o seu violão. Fizemos um churrasco e todas as mesas estavam postas embaixo de uma grande barraca. Arrumamos as malas e fomos para casa depois que a festa terminou. Foi muito divertido!

Language: Portuguese
Translated by: ???

Silver Box

Every item has some sort of meaning. Whether it's a priceless piece of diamond jewelry or an old and damaged photograph- everything has a story.

My great grandmother, Isabelle Gordon worked in the House of Commons in the Parliament Buildings when she was around seventeen years old. She had moved to Canada only about five years before, from Glasglow, Scotland. She was the oldest of six children so she had a lot of responsibility to support the family. The restaurant, in the House of Commons was where she worked. It was a fancy restaurant right in the middle of the Parliament Buildings. It was exclusive, and it was usually meant for Members of Parliament and their families. She may not have been a politician, but she worked very hard to help support her family.

The year was 1916- it was a cool, crisp February morning when a small fire started in the buildings. It probably started from a lit cigarette, but the cause quickly became unimportant as it quietly spread throughout the Centre block. Isabelle was there on the morning of the fire. She experienced the panic and sadness during the blaze. She went through the blazing cries of the lost lives. But, luckily, she escaped when a gracious soul helped her out the window. During the fire, people were rescuing valuable items by tossing them out windows. There was too much rich history in the Parliament buildings to be los,t so everybody was doing as much as they could to save every special item. They eventually realized that they had to flee the building before the flames got them too.

Since many items were damaged and had lost their value, the wife of the Senate decided to give them away to workers from the Parliament. She'd give away things like lamps and mirrors and other small items that were left behind. One of them was a small, elegant and stunning silver box. It was simple with a couple small details on it. The delicate antique was given to my great grandmother, as almost a gift for working hard at her job.

Today, the silver box is with my family, and it's been passed down two generations: from my great grandmother Isabelle Gordon, to my grandfather Gordon Saunders, and finally to my father, Alan Saunders. My family keeps interesting and historical items that belonged to my relatives in the box- from dog tags from my great grandfather in World War One, to his century old Swiss army knife.

The box itself is a piece of art. Small engraved tulips and leaves delicately decorate the bottom. It's singed on the corners, darkened, and shows its age, as a reminder of where it's been.

Everything has a story to tell and everything has memories. Even though this little box may not be worth a lot anymore, or it may not be the best preserved item from the fire, I see it as a beautiful piece of art that represents how my great grandmother contributed to the city and culture, and my family's history.

Hannah Saunders, Grade 8 Student

A caixa de prata.

Toda coisa tem um significado. Pode ser uma jóia preciosa ou uma fotografia veja. Cada coisa tem uma história.

A minha bisavó, Isabelle Gordon, trabalhava na Câmara dos Comuns, no Parlamento, quando tinha somente 17 anos. Tinha mudado ao Canadá cinco anos antes, desde Glasgow, Escócia. Ela era a maior de seis crianças, então tinha muita responsabilidade, para apoiar a família. Ela trabalhava no restaurante, onde era camarera e limpiava. Não era política, mas trabalhava forte para ajudar a sua família.

O ano era 1916 – numa manhã fria e clara, um incêndio começou no edifício. Províavelmente começou a causa dum cigarro, mas a causa foi rapidamente não importante, quando o incêndio creceu por o bloque central do Parlamento. Minha bisavó estava lá na manhã do incêndio, e sentiu o pánico e tristeza durante o incêndio. Fortunadamente, ela escapou quando alguem a ajudou sair pela janela. Durante o incêndio, as pessoas salvaram as coisas valorosas lançando-as pelas janelas. Havia tanta história rica nos edifícios do Parlamento, que todo mundo fez tanto possível para salvar qualquer coisa especial. Eles notaram que tinham que sair do edifício ante do que as chamas os atingirem também.

Visto que muitas coisas eram estragados, e tinham perdido o seu valor, a esposa do presidente do Senado decidiu dar estas coisas aos trabalhadores no Parlamento. Ela deu coisas como lâmpadas, espelhos e outras coisas pequenas. Uma dessas coisas foi uma caixa pequena linda, feita de prata. Foi muito simple, com algumas detalhas pequenas. Minha bisavó receveu esta antiguidade, um presente por ter trabalhado tão bem.

Hoje, a caixa de prata fica com minha família, e foi passada por duas gerações, de minha bisavó Isabelle Gordon, ao meu avô Gordon Saunders, e finalmente ao meu pai, Alan Saunders. Minha família guarda coisas interessantes e históricas na caixa, coisas que pertenecem a membros da família, como a carta de identificação do meu bisavô na guerra primeira mundial, e sua faca.

A caixa misma é arte, Pequenas folhas e tulipas decoram o fundo da caixa. Os cantos estão chamuscados, oscuros, e demostram a sua idad, uma lembrança da sua história.

Toda coisa tem uma história para contar, e toda coisa tem memórias. Mesmo que esta caixa pequena não tenha muito valor, e mesmo que não seja bem preservada, eu acho que é uma obra de arte que representa como a minha bisavó contribiu à cidade e sua cultura, e à história da minha familha.

Language: Portuguese
Translated by: Patricia Saunders

Hawthorne *Writes*
because everyone has a story...

19.   Romanian – Română

Of the estimated 23 million people in the world who speak Romanian, 20 million speakers live in Romania. It is spoken in Moldova, Russia, Serbia and Montenegro, and Ukraine, among other countries.

My Family

I'm an only child in my family. At home, I speak Romanian and English. I like to play with my little cars. I also love to ride my bicycle and scooter. I have a little dog that is black. His name is Kiki. I like to play with my dog and go hiking with my dad. I like helping my dad around the house especially when he's doing the lawn. My family is great and I like it when we all go to the theaters together.

Sergiu-Andrei Darida, Kindergarten Student

Sunt singurul copil din familie.
Acasă, eu vorbesc Romana și engleză.
I-mi place să mă joc cu mașinuțele,
și deasemenea i-mi place să mă plimb
cu bicicleta și cu trotineta.
Eu am un cățel mic negru. Numele lui
este Kiki. I-mi place să mă joc cu
el și să merg să-l plimb împreună
cu tata.
I-mi place să-mi ajut tată-l la trebu-
rile din jurul casei, în special când
tunde iarba.
Familia mea este minunată și-mi place
când mergem împreună la teatru.

Language : Romanian
Translated by : ???

My Favorite Thing

My favorite thing is better and smarter than any toy. My favorite thing is more fun, jumps higher and is worth much more than any toy. In fact my favorite thing is priceless. My favorite thing is five and a half years old. My favorite thing is fluffier than a longhaired puppy. My favorite thing can scare me and hurt me. My favorite thing can make me...

Sad when I'm mad...
　　Mad when I'm sad...
　　　Mad when I'm happy...
　　　　Happy when I'm mad...
　　　　　Sad when I'm happy...
Happy when I'm sad.
And make me feel bad and miserable.

My favorite thing has a favorite thing to. My favorite thing has feelings and friends.

My favorite thing can't live without me. I can't live without my favorite thing.

My favorite thing is like a person to me. It can talk to others of its type, get a laugh, cry, sneeze, cough, get a cold, get sick, learn, get hungry, thirsty and even get pregnant!!!

　　　Some people may be allergic to my favorite thing.
　　　　Some may want to be.
　　　Some people may like or love my favorite thing.
　　　　Some may not.
　　　My favorite thing may be allergic to you.
　　　　Or it may want to be.
　　　My favorite thing may like or love you.
　　　　Or it may not.

But I do know one thing! I LOVE MY FAVORITE THING AND MY FAVORITE THING LOVES ME! My Favorite thing is a

C

         A

                T

                        !!!

And she is better than any possible existing thing.

Julian Gramma, Grade 6 Student

Lucrul Peu Preferat

Lucrul meu preferat este mai bun si mai destept decit orice jucarie.
Lucrul meu preferat este mai jucaus, sare mai sus si este cu mult mai
scump decit orice jucarie. Ca atare , lucrul meu preferat nu are pret.
Lucrul meu preferat are 5 ani si jumate. Lucrul meu preferat este
mult mai pufos decit orice catelus. Lucrul meu preferat poate sa ma
sperie si sa ma zgirie. Lucrul meu preferat poate sa ma faca

    Trist cind sint suparat

        Suparat cind sint trist

           Suparat cind sint vesel

              Vesel cint sint suparat

                  Trist cind sint vesel

                    Si vesel cind sint

trist.....

Lucrul meu preferat are si el lucru sau preferat. Lucrul meu preferat
are sentimente si prieteni.

Lucrul meu preferat nu poate trai fara mine. Nici eu nu pot trai fara el.

Lucrul meu preferat este ca o personalitate pentru mine. El poate sa
vorbeasca cu altii in felul lui, sa rida, sa plinga, sa starnute, sa tuseasca,
sa se imbolnaviasca, sa invete, sa-i fie foame, sa-i fie sete , si ciar sa
aiba bebelusi!!!

           Unii pot sa fie allergici la lucrul meu
preferat.

           Altii vor sa fie.

        Unor persoane poate sa le placa sau ciar sa iubeasca
lucrul meu preferat.

           Altor nu.

           Lucrul meu preferat poate sa -ti fie
allergic.

           Sau ar vrea sa fie.

        Lucrului meu preferat ii poti placea sau el poate ciar
sa te iubeasca.

           Sau poate nu.

Dar un lucru stiu! IMI IUBESC LUCRUL MEU PREFERAT SI
LUCRUL MEU PREFERAT MA
IUBESTE PE MINE! Lucrul Meu Preferat este o

                                          P
                                        I
                                      C
                                    I
                                  C
                                A
                                  !!!

Si ea este cea mai buna decit orice poate exista!

Language: Romanian
Translated by: ???

Hawthorne *Writes*
because everyone has a story...

YOUR FUTURE IS NOW

20.   Russian – Русский

An estimated 145 million people in the world speak Russian as a first language. 110 million people speak Russian as a second language. Outside of Russia, this language is also spoken in Kyrgyzstanm, Belarus, Ukraine, and the United States.

My Grandfather's Medals

Bloody wounds gaping open, infected by the dirt and dust swirling around at all times. Limbs torn to shreds by the howling bombs, hanging on to the body by mere threads. The patients with hope in their eyes, unaware that there is no hope for their scarred and injured bodies.

My grandfather, Dr. Zelman Dubovitsky, experienced all of that. He served as a student doctor in Leningrad during World War II, taking care of wounded soldiers who were evacuated from the battlefront. He would help them off the trains and into the hospital, where they would be cared for. He also looked after some patients.

My grandfather served as a naval aviation doctor in the Soviet Armed Forces for many years, and in recognition of his time and effort, my grandfather was awarded numerous medals. Dr. Dubovitsky received medals for serving in the navy as well as to commemorate the end of World War II.

His first medal was for his service with the Leningrad defence forces during the Germans' attack. It smells very metallic and a bit musty, like all of the older medals. It is now a tad worn, the medal itself is starting to get dull. The ribbon is olive green with darker green stripes. It is fraying a bit, but still means as much as it did the day that my grandfather received it, the first medal he ever got.

Dr. Dubovitsky got his second medal for the USSR's victory over Germany in 1945. This medal is very important to my grandfather, as it signifies a great triumph over a strong enemy. This medal has a black and orange striped ribbon that you can tell has faded a bit, but the medal is still very brilliant.

My grandfather's third medal was for his first ten years of military service. It is silver-coloured with a silvery-grey ribbon edged in yellow. For fifteen years of service, my grandfather received an Order of the Red Star. It is a pin shaped like a red star, and in the centre is a silver disc engraved with images of soldiers.

In addition to these four honours, Dr. Dubovitsky has been given five medals for meritorious service, and five medals commemorating the anniversary of the victory of the USSR in World War II. Whenever I look at these five medals, I am very proud of my grandfather for fighting for what he believed in, and I am always extremely grateful that he survived those dreadful years of war.

Dr. Dubovitsky has a stunning total of thirteen medals and one order. I am sure that not many people can boast that their grandfathers have that many medals. I am incredibly proud of what my grandfather has achieved over the years, and he is one of my heroes. We should all remember the sacrifices that the older generation has made so that we can live in peace.

Lilia Lockwood, Grade 7 Student

Дедушкины медали

Зияющие кровоточащие раны, инфицированные грязью и постоянной, вездесущей пылью. Висящие на волоске конечности, раздробленнные воющими бомбами. Больные с надеждой в глазах, не сознающие, что для их израненных и изуродованных тел надежды уже не осталось.

Мой дедушка, доктор Зельман Дубовицкий, всё это испытал. Он был курсантом-медиком в Ленинграде во время Второй мировой войны и ухаживал за эвакуированными с фронта ранеными. Он помогал выносить их с поезда и транспортировать в госпиталь, где они должны были проходить лечение. Он также ухаживал за больными.

Мой дедушка много лет служил в советских Вооруженных Силах врачом медицинской службы морской авиации и получил много медалей за выслугу лет и боевые заслуги. Доктор Дубовицкий был награжден и за службу в военно-морских силах, и за победу во Второй мировой войне.

Он получил свою первую медаль за участие в обороне Ленинграда во время наступления немецких войск. Как и у всех старых медалей, у этой медали запах металла и старины. Она выглядит немного потертой, и сама медаль уже потускнела. Ленточка —оливково-зеленого цвета с полосками потемнее. Она немного изношена, но и сейчас она значит для него столь же много как и в тот день, когда мой дедушка получил её, свою самую первую медаль.

Свою вторую медаль Доктор Дубовицкий получил за победу СССР над Германией в 1945 году. Эта медаль имеет очень большое значение для дедушки, так как она символизирует триумфальную победу над могучим врагом. У этой медали ленточка с черными и оранжевыми полосками, которая немного выцвела, но сама медаль всё ещё ярко блестит.

Свою третью медаль дедушка получил за первые десять лет военной службы. Она серебристого цвета на серебристо-серой ленточке, окаймлённой желтыми полосками. За пятнадцать лет службы дедушку наградили Орденом Красной Звезды. Эта награда сделана в форме красной звезды, в центре которой расположен серебряный диск с выгравированными образами солдат.

Кроме этих четырех наград доктор Дубовицкий получил пять медалей за безупречную службу и пять юбилейных медалей за победу СССР во Второй мировой войне. Когда я смотрю на эти пять медалей, меня охватывает огромное чувство гордости за моего дедушку, который воевал за то, во что он верил, и я всегда так благодарна, что он выжил в те страшные годы войны.

У доктора Дубовицкого потрясающее количество наград — тринадцать медалей и один орден. Я уверена, что немногие могут похвастаться дедушкой, у которого было бы столько медалей. Я невероятно горжусь тем, чего достиг мой дедушка за годы своей жизни — он герой в моих глазах. Мы все должны помнить те жертвы, которые принесли люди старшего поколения, чтобы мы могли жить в мире.

Лилия Локвуд

Language : Russian
Translated by : Eugenia Lockwood

Living With Sickle Cell Anemia

My name is Neisha Marshall-Guthrie. I am eleven years old and I was born on January 18th, 1995. I was diagnosed with sickle cell anemia when I was one year old. Sickle cell anemia is hereditary. This means that you have to get the gene from both parents to have the disease. Sickle cell anemia is a blood disorder that affects hemoglobin, a protein found in red blood cells that help carry oxygen throughout the body.

Hemoglobin S ('S' stands for sickle) is the type of hemoglobin people with sickle cell conditions make. Hemoglobin S does not live as long as normal hemoglobin. It lives for about 16 days. The hemoglobin becomes stiff which makes it hard to pass through the body's blood vessels.

Some of the symptoms are pain in your chest, arms, legs, or stomach. If the pain gets very bad, I have to see the doctor otherwise I stay at home and have to eat a lot. I have had to go to the hospital quite a few times. I get a needle when I go and I also receive intravenous, which is when a needle is inserted into your veins and then the needle is attached to a tube which leads to a bag filled with a clear liquid. The clear liquid goes into my bloodstream. I have to stay in the hospital over one or two nights until I am well enough to go home. The last time I was hospitalized was just over a year ago.

Even though I have sickle cell anemia, I live a healthy normal life.

Neisha Marshall-Guthrie, Grade 5 Student

Жизнь с серповидно-клеточной анемией

Меня зовут Нейша Маршалл-Гатри. Мне одиннадцать лет. Я родилась 18 января 1995 года. Когда мне был один год, у меня обнаружили серповидно-клеточную анемию. Серповидно-клеточная анемия — наследственная болезнь. Это значит, что эта болезнь бывает у тех, кто получил этот ген от обоих родителей. Серповидно-клеточная анемия — это заболевание крови, поражающее гемоглобин, белок, находящийся в красных кровяных тельцах, который переносит кислород по всему телу. Гемоглобин типа С (от слова «серповидный) производится организмом людей, болеющих этой анемией. Гемоглобин С живет не так долго, как нормальный гемоглобин. Он живет примерно 16 дней. Такой гемоглобин становится жестким, что затрудняет его прохождение через кровеносные сосуды.

Некоторые из симптомов болезни — это боли в груди, руках, ногах или желудке. Если боль очень сильная, мне надо идти к врачу, а если нет, то я остаюсь дома, и мне необходимо усиленное питание. Мне уже не раз пришлось побывать в больнице. Там мне делают укол и внутривенное вливание, когда иглу вставляют в вену, а игла соединяется с трубкой, ведущей к сумке с прозрачной жидкостью. Эта прозрачная жидкость вливается в мою кровеносную систему. Я остаюсь в больнице на день или два, пока не начинаю чувствовать себя достаточно хорошо, чтобы вернуться домой. Последний раз меня госпитализировали немногим года назад.

Несмотря на то, что у меня серповидно-клеточная анемия, я веду нормальный, здоровый образ жизни.

Language: Russian
Translated by: Eugenia Lockwood

The Birth of Me!

My dad was working at the hospital – he's a doctor. At the end of July, he got two days off. At that time my mom was pregnant. So my parents decided to go to my grandma's village and then go fishing because my dad loves fishing. That day my mom met her friend. Her friend asked, "When is the baby going to be born?"

My mom said, "Right away!" but she was only joking for she knew it was too early for me to be born. That's one of the reasons why they felt comfortable with the decision to go to my grandma's village.

My parents went to sleep at 10 in the evening because they had to wake up early. My parents woke up when the sun was just starting to rise. They drank some tea. My dad took his car and his boat and went fishing. Because it was early, my mom was really tired. She tried to fall asleep but she couldn't. At 8 in the morning, there was something wrong. She told her mom (my grandma) that the baby was arriving that day. My grandma was really scared, because in small village hospitals, there wouldn't be any doctors since July 27th (now it is July 1st) was the day of Independence in the Republic of Belarus. My grandma went to her brother to ask if he cold go to the lake to get my dad. When he got there, he realized that my dad was in the middle of the lake. He tried yelling and screaming, but no matter how hard he tried, my dad couldn't hear him. To his luck, he had a speaker phone in his car. So he used the speaker phone to tell my dad that his wife was going to give birth to me. At that point, my dad had caught 3 big fish – what luck! When he heard my grandma' brother, he rowed the boat to the shore as fast as he could.

When my dad came back, my parents went to the place of the gynecology specialist. She said that my mom had to go to the closest hospital. My parents didn't have time to go to the city (Minsk, which was 1.5 hours away by car). The closest hospital was 30 km away.

At 12:15 p.m. I was born in a small town hospital. Instead of crying when I was born, I said "da" which means "yes" in Russian. So I was born unexpectedly on July 27th, 1994.

The number 27 is the lucky number for my family. It is lucky because I was born on July 27th, my parents got married on November 27th, and we moved to Canada on November 27th! You can't image how fun it is to celebrate your parent's anniversary on an airplane!

Every lucky thing that has happened to my family was unexpected. And it always happened on the same date: the 27th! I hope that in the future my luck will continue to come on the 27th!

Alesia Bakhanovich, Grade 5 Student

"Как я родилась"
(Title)

Мой папа работал в госпитале. Он - доктор. В конце июля он имел два выходных дня. В это время моя мама была беременна. Мои родители решили поехать к бабушке в деревню, затем на рыбалку потомучто мой папа любит рыбачить. В этот же день моя мама встретила подругу и она спросила: "Когда родится ребёнок?" Моя мама сказала: "Хоть сейчас". Она конечно не шутила. Она знала, что еще слишком рано для рождения ребенка. Это была причина, почему, что они чувствовали себя уверенно с решением поехать в деревню.

Мои родители легли спать в 10 вечера, потомучто рано утром они должны были вставать. Мои родители проснулись с рассветом солнца. Они выпили чай. Мой папа взял машину, лодку и поехал рыбачить. Было еще рано и моя мама чувствовала усталость. Она пыталась уснуть, но не смогла. К восьми утра она поняла, что что не так. Она сказала своей маме, что ребенок хочет появиться на свет сегодня. Моя бабушка была встревожена, потомучто в маленькой больнице в деревне не будет ни одного доктора, ведь это был еще и праздник - день независимости республики Беларусь

Моя бабушка пошла к своему брату спросить, если он сможет поехать на озеро позвать моего папу.

Когда бабушкин брат добрался до озера, он увидил, что мой папа был на середине озера. Он попытался звать, кричать, но мой папа не слышал его. Тогда бабушкин брат вспомнил, что у него есть громкоговоритель в машине. Он сказал по громкоговорителю, что ребенок скоро должен родиться. Мой папа к этому времени уже поймал при больших рыбы. Когда он услышал, что сказал бабушкин брат, он быстро развернул лодку и со всей силы погреб к берегу.

Когда мой папа вернулся, мои родители поехали домой к акушерке. Она сказала, что мои родители должен ехать в ближайшую больницу. Мои родители не имели время добраться до города, где они жили. До Минска было 1,5 часа езды. Ближайшая больница находилась в 30 км.

В 12.^{15} я была рождена в роддоме в маленьком городе. Вместо плача, когда я только родилась, я сказала „Да". Я родилась неожиданно 27 июля 1994 года.

Число 27 - счастливое число для нашей семьи. Я была рождена в июле 27,^{20} мои родители поженились в ноябре 27,^{20} и мы приехали в Канаду в ноябре 27.^{20} Можете представить какая радость праздновать годовщину свадьбы на самолёте.

Каждое радостное событие, которое случилось в моей семье, было ножиданным. И всегда это случалось 27 числа. Я надеюсь, что в будущем моя удача будет приходить ко мне 27 числа.

Language: Russian
Translated by: Viacheslav Bakhanovich

Hawthorne *Writes*
because everyone has a story...

21. Scots Gaelic - Gàidhlig

Scottish Gaelic is spoken by an estimated 60 thousand people. Most speakers live in in the United Kingdom, however, some speakers also live in Australia, Canada, and the United States.

The Girl in the Corner

The issue of bullying is endlessly addressed in schools and has yet to be diminished. Why? I cannot speak for bullies, however, I can relate my tale of such matters...

In my school, I was the only eight-year-old that had nobody to play with! Every recess, I spent in our yard's furthest corner reading. This was not because I loved solitude, nobody seemed to like me. I became "the girl in the corner". Endlessly, I observed the "popular girls" in their hideout playing fabulous games. I watched trends change and lonesomly wished I could be a member of their executive club. One bright day I ceased my chance.

The momentary style was collecting small stuffed animals attached to keychains. These were toted everywhere and used to enter the "club" alongside a mysterious password. I owned an adorable stuffed tiger on a keychain. The next day I hastily brought it to school and made my presence obvious. For twenty minutes I sat in the yard and was almost ready to give up when, to my joy, the club's messenger Sara G., sauntered up and asked me to play. I graciously accepted and off I went, happy as can be. The password was "daisy" and as it was recited, I proudly showed my tiger. It was actually a trap. The moment I stepped onto their territory, the group gathered round me and the leader, Sarah E., exclaimed " Why do you think you can come here? Just because you have a keychain does not mean you are accepted. You are nobody." Turning to her followers she jeered " Get her out of here, NOW!" Without a word I was pushed onto the pavement. No use telling the teacher. This group consisted of her pets and she would not believe the likes of me. I went home, sullen and sad, wrapped myself up in a sheet and tried, with all of my heart, to disappear. My mother was perplexed. "Is something wrong?" " I am nobody you know..." I answered in earnest. Soon all of my troubles were pouring unto her.

We spoke to my teacher the next day to no avail. At break, I sat under the basketball nets and cried. Sarah E. and company just laughed and watched, pretending to eat popcorn as if enjoying a film. I saw red. The issue was taken to the Principal, who postponed speaking with us for as long as possible and to the school council, a waste of breath. Bullying incidents carried on and, shortly afterwards, I left the school and received education from home for the remainder of the year.

This story has a happy ending. Last year, I entered the gifted program at Hawthorne Public School. Now I have many friends and it is our policy not to bully. However, I never felt closure. Contrary to the popular belief " never run from your problems", sometimes one has to escape from their troubles and let the fire burn itself out...

Sarah Beale, Grade 7 Student

An Nighean 'san Oisean:

Tha na daoine an còmhnaidh a' bruidhinn air na pulaidhean, ach chan eil iad a' faighinn fuasgladh. Carson? Chan eil mi a' labhairt air son na pulaidh, ach tha sgeul agam air…

Anns an sgoil agam, bha mi an aon pàisde d'ochd bliadhna gun chompanach-cluiche. Eadar clasaichean, bha mi a' leughadh anns an oisean as fhaide air falbh. Cha robh air son chord a' leughadh rium, no an uaigneas. Bha air son dìth caraid orm. Faigh mi an ainm "an nighean 'san oisean". Là air là gun cheann, chunnaic mi na nigheanan coitean-tan anns an àite-falaich a' cluiche an geamaichean iongantachan, agus iad a' caochladh leis an aimsir. Bha mi riamh ag iarraidh a bhith ball a' chlub aca. Aon là briagha, faigh mi an cothrom.

Bha fasan an là a bhith a' cruinneachadh slabhraidhean-iuchair agus ainmhidhean dé-ideagan oirre. Le facal-faire agus an tìgear agam, dh'fheith mi gus an d'thàinig c, teach-daire na chlub. An robh mi ag iarraidh a bhith a' cluiche? Gu dearbh, tapadh leibh! Agus sinn air falbh. Bha 'neòinean' am facal-faire. Chan mi am facal agus dh'fhoillsich mi an tìgear. Ach bha ribe a bh'ann. As a' bhad, chruinnich na nigheanan mi. Ghlaodh Mórag, an toiseach, "Carson tha thu a' smaoineachadh gum faod thu tighinn an seo? Chan eil an slabhraidh-iuchair an iuchair fhéin d'ar chlub! Chan tusa té sam bith! Thalla!" D'a chàirdean dh'innis i "A mach leatha!"

Gan fhacal, bhrùth iad mi air a' cabhsair. Cha do dh'inns' mi an tidsear — bha a h-uile nighean a peatan. Cha bhith i gam chreidsinn.

Chaidh mi dhachaidh brònach muladach. Bha mi ag iarraidh a bhith nam bhàsachadh. Cheil mi fhì fo'n aodach-leapa.

"Dé tha dol?" dh'innse mo mhathair.

" 'S mise neo-ni," arsa mise. Gu luath bha mo thrioblaidean nochta.

An ath là, chunnaic sinn an tidsear, ach cha robh cothrom air. An déidh mo chla-saichean, shuidh mi fo'n lìon bascaidbhall, agus chaoin mi. Ni

Mórag agus an còmhlan gàire agus faire. Leig iad air gu'n robh iad ag ithe suiteas aig an taigh-dhealbh. Chuir e fearg orm.

Chaidh sinn aig am prìomh-thidsear, agus e gar seachnadh. Rinn a' chomhairle-sgoil rud 'sam bith. Lean na pulaidhean mar sin. An ùin gheàrr, dh'fhàg mi a' sgoil. Dh'ionnsaich mo mhathair mi gu deireadh am bliadhna.

Ach thàinig mo sgeul gu crìoch shona. Thòisich mi an uiridh am prògram air son sgoilear comasach aig an sgoil Hawthorne. An drasda, tha iomadh cairdean agam, ach feumaidh na pulaidhean bith modhail. Gidheadh cha robh mi riamh sàsaichte.

An aghaidh nan sheanfhacal "Na ruith o'r trioblaidean," air uiribh faodaidh tu an teine a teicheadh gus an loisg e gu talamh.

Language: Scots Gaelic
Translated by: Douglas McKearken

Hawthorne *Writes*
because everyone has a story...

YOUR FUTURE IS NOW

22.   Serbo-Croatian –
Srpskohrvatski

Sarajevo to Ottawa

It's 1991. An ethnic war broke out and it went down in history as one of the deadliest blood baths of all time. She took her baby, got in the car with her husband and six-year-old daughter, and left.

My mother was born on February 21, 1963 in Sarajevo, Bosnia and Herzegovina. She was always the smart one in her family, so they expected nothing more than the best. She grew up in Sarajevo, which was a city of many religions: Eastern Orthodoxy, Islam, Roman Catholicism, and Judaism. In 1991, when I was born, war broke out of its box of peace which was locked up for some forty years. My mother and my father knew they had to leave as soon as they heard gun shots.

We arrived in Offenbach, Germany, and it was going to be our new home. You would think that was great, but that would be wide of the mark. My father went back to Sarajevo to earn a little more money of what was left of his bank that he had worked in. Back in Germany, we'd hear, "Massacre in Sarajevo!" and our hearts would sink every time. Life was tough in Germany, especially for my mother, who had two youngsters in both her hands. It was difficult, until my father came back from Sarajevo. Then, everything went back to normal.

After six years, my parents decided to leave Germany and Europe and move to Canada, which turned out to be the best decision we've ever made. Life is great in Canada – what's not to like? It's clean, it's a place of great opportunities and it's safe. We arrived in Ottawa, Canada in 1998 and everything was miraculous from that point on.

I consider my mother as my greatest hero. Both of my parents left everything behind to give my sister and I better opportunities and a better life. She saved my life. In 1991, when I was born, she took me, got in the car with her husband and six-year-old daughter, and left.

Djordje Djuric, Grade 8 Student

1991 godina. Počinje okrutan rat. Ona je uzela svoju bebu i 6-godini staru kćerku i otišla sa mužem i djecom.

Moja mama je rođena 21. Feb. 1963 u Sarajevu, Bosna i Hercegovina. Bila je uvijek pametna. Rođjena je u Sarajevu, što ima puno religija: Hrišćana, Muslimana, Jevreja. 1991 godina, kada sam ja bila rođen mir se raspuknuo i moji roditeli su znali da moraju da napuste svoj grad.

Došli smo u Njemačku, u grad Offenbach. Moj otac je neko vrijeme bio u Sarajevu, a onda se vratijo, i živio u Njemačku sa nas. Poslije 6 godina odlučic smo da napustimo Njemačku i odemo u Kanadu. To je bila jako dobra odluka. Život u kanadi je dobar. Sve je čisto, svakima šansu da živi dobro, i sigurno je. Šta drugo bi čovjek poželio? Došli smo u kanada 1998, od tada, sve nam ide dobro.

Moja mama je moj heroj. Moji roditel su ostaviti sve i došli ovdje da ja i moja sestra imamo priliku, da živimo dobro.

Ona je spasila moj život u 1991 godine, uzela je mene, uzela moje sestru i moj tata i mama fer napusti grad.

Language: Serbo-Croatian
Translated by: Djordje Djuric, Grade 8 Student

Keepsake Treasures

We have a very special keepsake in our family. That keepsake is our grandfather clock, which was passed down to my mother from her grandfather. He originally purchased the clock in 1989 before he passed away in 2000. He was excited about it and whenever I went to visit him, he would open up the clock to show me the keys. When I was four I really liked cars and keys. The clock is green and shaped like a box. It has a red velvet lining and there are keys hanging inside. When you open the clock's door, you can put car keys, house keys and bike keys inside.

The grandfather clock was given to my mother when her father died. It is very special to her because it is a memory of her father and the good times they shared.

The clock will be passed down to me and I will then keep this treasure unit I die. I, in turn, will leave it to my first-born child.

Today my mother keeps our special clock in her room up high on the dresser in her bedroom. That makes me realize how important it is to her, as she wants to make sure it is safe and sound.

Brandon Cain, Grade 8 Student

Mi imamo nešto što je blago u našu familiu. To blago je moj dedin sat. Moj deda je dao tje sat da moju mamu. on je kupio sat u 1989, i onda je umro u 2000. Njemo je bila drago kada ja dodem daga vidim. Kada sam ja bio četri, ja sam volio aure i kučeve. Sat je zelen i izgleda kao kočka. Sat ima cervcni somot, i ima ključeve unutru.

Moj deda je dao sat mojoj mama kada je on umro. To je ono blago za nje, zato što ta podsetiti nje kako su oni se imali dobre vreme.

Sat će bit dat to mene, i ja ću dati moje dete kada ja umrem.

Danas moja mama ima taj sat u njezinu sobu i ja i ona kladamo svaki dan.

Language: Serbo-Croatian
Translated by: Djordje Djuric, Grade 8 Student

Hawthorne *Writes*
because everyone has a story...

YOUR FUTURE IS NOW

23. Somali – Soomaaliga

Somali is spoken by nearly 13 million people around the world. Most Somali speakers live in Somalia, but it is also spoken in Djibouti, Ethiopia, Kenya and the United Kingdom.

My Goalie Gloves

Shiny, silver, smooth, lots of grip with a big Nike sign that are my goalie gloves. My goalie gloves are the most important things to me and it is my favourite thing next to my soccer cleats. I have done many excellent saves with my gloves. I got my gloves about two years ago and they are priceless, and I wouldn't trade it for anything in the world. I bought the gloves because people always said I was good in goalie and it got me motivated. Also, because my teammates said I was really good and it looked fun and exciting.

Then one day I asked my dad to get me gloves and he did. Before the season had started I was practicing with my brothers outside and inside my house in the basement so I can be the best. Also I went to play with my father sometimes and played goalie for him and his friends while they played. In the first game, we faced one of the worst teams in the league and I got a shutout thanks to my defenders.

Four weeks into the season my team was undefeated and I had four shutouts. In the last game we faced our biggest rivals and I played hard and dived everywhere so the ball wouldn't go in. But then my defenders did an error and then scored on me. That was the most heart-breaking moment but it didn't really matter because we advanced to playoffs.

In the playoffs we faced the worst team and we won. Then we advanced to the semis and won again. Our coach was so happy that we won and he took us out for a dinner. In the finals, we were up against the team, which beat us 1-0 and now was the time for us to get our revenge. Before the game I was practicing so hard and I was getting pumped up for the finals. My dad and the coach were kicking on me to get me working hard. By the late afternoon around 5:30 the game started and I was nervous because it was my first year as a goalie and I didn't have much experience. By the first half there wasn't that much action but my team was leading 1-0. In the second half, the other team started playing hard and aggressive. They were taking so much shots on me but I saved all of them or they went over the net. There was like five minutes left and I was waiting for that whistle. After that five minutes it was all over we were the champs all because of my skills and gloves. I would never trade it for anything in the world.

Dirie Dahir, Grade 8 Student

Glaviiskheya Goolheya

Waa galin, waax dhadaalaaya. Waxaa ku yaab calaamad weyn oo Nike. Waxaa warqaan glau-iske goolhaya. Wa waax aad u qima badan. Glaviska qolaal badan ayaan kuu gabtey. Waxaan haystey labo sanadaad, waa waax aan lai'pbstaren. Waxaan uu Ptsaady daadlu waray Pyo dhahan waad ku Pemartahay Pyo waxaanu dhaa xPsaxPisa badan.

Maalin waxaan wey dPPyey aabahay Pnu ei soo Pitaya. Waxaan ba cPyaan Pitray aabahay Pyo saaxPbadii. Intaanu cPyaarti bilaaban waan tababaranayey. cPyaarti hore waxaan kaa cPyaarnay kooxde ogu xumaa.

Afaar wakhtiyaal aan koox dayne. cPyaarti ugu dambaysay waxaanu la kulanay kooxdii ugu adkayd. Waxaan ku boodayey meel walba sPaan u gabto. kubada. Dabadeed ra Ptraaceenie ayaa si khalad ah nagu dhaliyey, lakin cPyaartii ugu dambayso ayaan tagnay.

cPyaartii ugu dambaysana waxaan cPyarnay cPyaartay ugu xumaa. Pyo wanu badinahay.

Tabarahayaga aad buu farhay, waxaanu nageeye casho. Ciyaarti labad aan waxaanu la ciyaamay koordii hore noga badisay. Waxaanu doonayney innaanu ka aarsano, oo ka badino. Maantoodan ayaan tobab- araneyey. Markii wakhte la gaaray waan yara baqday, sababtoo ah waa sanadkii gaalhey igu horeysay. Qabtii hore koordayda horeysey. Qabtii labaad koordii kale wakay ku belaabeena werer cday, lakiin wan ista gabtay goolashii. Shanti dasigo ee ugu dambaysay waxaan sagayad siidihii. Markiiba anagaa badinay, sababtan waxaa laha aqootayd iyo glaviiski ficaan. ~~Waxa~~ Waar kale kumo doors- anayo gloviiskaya

Language: Somali
Translated by: Sagal Djama, Grade 8 Student

My Life

My life is a very good life because it is fun. When I was really little, I didn't have to go to school. I liked it when I didn't have to go to school because school can be boring. I liked daycare better than school because all we did was play, but, when I got bigger, I had to go to school.

"Mom, do I have to go to school?" I asked tiredly.

"Yes, you do, Samaleh. Do you want to be smart or not?" replied my mother.

"I don't care," I mumbled.

"Get on the bus," commanded my mother.

When I got to school, I was shy of everyone in my class. I met a boy named Malcolm and we became best friends and I started to like school.

In Grade 2, my teacher, Mrs. Labonte, was a nice teacher. I liked it because it was fun in Mrs. Labonte's class. In Grade 3, Miss Menzies was my teacher and it was cool in her class. I really liked Grade 3 and I miss it. In Grade 4 with Mrs. Cinkant, I like gym the best. In gym we do cool basketball drills and I am trying out for the basketball team. I would really like to be on the basketball team.

Samaleh Daher, Grade 4 Student

Noloshayda

Noloshayda waa nolol aad uwanaagsan, aadna ufiican. Markii aanyaraa ma aana aadi jirin iskuul. Ma aanan jeclayn aadista iskuulka, iskuulka waan ku caajisaa waxaan kajeclahay xanaanada sabab too ah waan iska cayaarna xanaanada markii aan waynaayday waa inaan iskuulka aado. Hooyaday waxaankudhahaa.

" Iskuulma inaan aada?" anigoo caajis ah

Markas bay tiraahdaa,"haa, marabtid miyaa inaad wiil caqlileh noqotid?"

Waxaan ku iraah, "daa makala jecli"

Markaas baytiraahdaa, "raac baska" kucelcelisaa hooyaday.

Markii aan kadagay buska oon tagay iskuulka anigoo aadd uxishoonaya qofkasta oo galaska kamid ah baan waxaan isbaranay wiil Malcolm ladhaho waxaana noqonay saaxiibo aad iskufiican. Iskuulkiina waan jecladay.

Language: Somali
Translated by: International Language Program

Hawthorne *Writes*
because everyone has a story...

YOUR FUTURE IS NOW

24.   Spanish – Español

Spanish

Spanish, or Castilian, is an Iberian Romance language. It is spoken by an estimated 400 million people worldwide and is the official language of 23 countries. It originated in Spain and was brought to the Americas and other parts of the world by Spanish explorers during the last 500 years. Spanish is not the ONLY language spoken in Spain. There are in fact 3 other languages and many other dialects spoken there. An interesting note is the influence of the Arabic language in the evolution of Spanish over the years. Approximately 5000 words are of Arabic origin.

Although there are slight differences in sounds and idioms from country to country, for the most part, the Spanish spoken in each country is universal. Spanish follows similar grammatical rules to Portuguese, French and Italian. It reads from left to write. The traditional Spanish alphabet contains 27 letters, each of which represents a specific sound. The only silent letter in Spanish is the "h". Accents are used to place the stress on a specific syllable, but they do not change the sound of the letter on which they are placed.

Español

El español, o castellano, es una lengua romance del grupo ibérico. Es hablado por unos 400 miliones de personas en el mundo y es la lengua oficial de 23 países. El español se originaba en España, pero los exploradores españoles trayeron la lengua a las Américas y a otras partes del mundo durante los últimos 500 años. El español no es la única lengua que se habla en España. En efecto, se hablan tres otras lenguas y varios dialectos también. Es interesante notar la influencia Arábica en el español. Hay aproximadamente 5000 palabras de origen arábica.

Aunque se encuentren ligeras diferencias en los sonidos y los modismos de país en país, por la mayor parte, el español que se habla en cada país es universal. El español sigue reglas gramaticales semejantes al italiano, al portugués y al francés. Se lee de izquierda a derecha. El alfabeto español contiene 27 letras y cada una representa un sonido especifico. La única letra muda es el "h". Se usan los acentos normalmente para hacer hincapié en ciertas sílabas, pero no cambian el sonido de la letra en la cual estan colocados.

Language Description and Translation by: Kelly Stanutz-Sedlar, Intermediate Teacher

My mom's childhood memories of Hawthorne Public School

As I walk down the long white hallways of Hawthorne Public School, I wonder about the students who have traveled in my footsteps before me. What were their impressions of this place? Did they like it here? How many of them made those scary steps down the hallway to the principal's office after getting into some kind of trouble and what were the consequences they faced? And alas, I have to wonder no more. All I have to do is ask Shannon Murphy, one very special student who attended this school a long time ago. And why is she so special you maybe asking yourself – well she just happens to be my mom.

I hope she won't object to me telling you this but my mom is now 35 years old.   She was born on February 11 1971 at The Grace Hospital in Ottawa/Ontario (I don't even think that it exists anymore). She now works for the Health care as a Personal Support Worker.

Shannon Glenna Murhphy started her days at Hawthorne Public School in 1975.   That was in the last century! My mom attended Hawthorne from 1975 to 1984. She started in junior kindergarten and went right through to grade 8. And I, her first born, eldest son will follow proudly in her bold footsteps.

When I ask her if and how Hawthorne has changed in the last 30 years, she most definitely assures me it has. The teachers are different, well though they probably have similar personalities; their faces are not the same. As for the curriculum, my mother says that it is undoubtedly more demanding. I am sure that I get more homework than what she did!

One thing that is the same is Mrs. Hurtubise (the office administrator). She is still working at the office. Maybe she remembers a cute little girl by the name of Shannon Murphy.

 The school hours were also different when my when my mom was a student here. Back in 1975 the school day began at 9am and ended at

3pm or 3:15pm. However, my mom didn't have to rush to school in the mornings because she lived down the street from Hawthorne

As for the school activities, I'm sure we have a few different things now, but some things remain the same. For instance my mom was on the volleyball team and she was in the choir.

Naturally my mom was quite popular in school she, had many friends. And one of her most distinctive memories is her graduation. After leaving Hawthorne and she attended Canterbury High School.

Though up until now I have followed my mom's childhood path, I will not be attending the same high school as she did. I will hopefully be going to Hillcrest – my mom's choice not necessarily mine.

Treye Murphy, Grade 7 Student

Cuando yo camino a lo largo de los corredores blancos de la escuela publica de Hawthorn, yo pregunto a los estudiantes que han viajado en mis pasos ante de mi. ¿Ellos tienen gusto aquí? ¿Cuantos sus impresiones de este place? ¿Cuantos de ellos hicieron pasos abajo del vestíbulo al oficina de principal de conseguir un cierta clase de apuro y. ¿Cales las consecuencias que hicieron frente? Yo no preguntado no más. Todos que tengo que hacer debo pedir Shanon Murphy, una estudiante mí espéciale que atendió este esquela de largo tiempo pasee. Y porque es ella si especial- ella es mi madre.

Yo espera ella no opones decir ustedes pero mi mama ahora 35 anos. Ella llevar febrero 11 1971 en hospital de Grace Ottawa Ontario (yo no pensar que existir). Ella trabajo para salud como uno personal ayuda trabajo.

Shanon Glenna Murphy comenzado sus días en la escuela publica de Hawthorn en 1975. ¡Este era en el paso siglo! Mi madre atendió Hawthorn de 1975 a 1984. Ella comenzado en kindergarten y paseo a grado ocho. Y yo, el primero llevado, el mas viejo niño seguirá orgulloso en sus pasos.

Como yo pida ella si y como Hawthorn este cambiad en el paseo 30 anos, ella mas azures yo que tienen el mismo personalices; ellos caras es diferente. En cuanto al plan de estudios, es más exigente. Yo es seguro que yo consiga más asignaciones que ella.

Una cosa que es el mismo es Maestra Hurtubise (el es oficina administrador). Ella es aun trabajo en la oficina. Quizá ella recuerde una niña del nombre Shanon Murphy.

El escuela ores es diferente también cuando mí madre este una estudiante aquí. En 1975 el día de escuela comenzado en 9am y terminado en 3pm o 3:15pm. Sin embargo mi madre puede no acometidas en el mañana porque el viva debajo de la acalle de Hawthorn.

Por la escuela actividades, yo es seguro que un poquito es diferente, pero algunas siguen siendo iguales. Por caso mi madre este en equipe de voleibol y en el coro.

Naturalmente mi madre este muy popular en escuela ella, hay muchos amigos. Y una de ellas muy buena memoria este el graduación. Después Hawthorn ella atendido el escuela Gateburry. A un que encima este momento de mi seguido la niñez de mi mama no atendré a la mismo escuela que ella. Yo vaya a Hilcrest. Mi mama es bién escogida.

Language: Spanish
Translated by:

My Cloudy Memory

To tell you about my favourite childhood memory, I have to go way back to the summer of 1967. I was five years old at the time (I guess I just gave away my age) and Canada was turning 100. That summer, the entire country was in the throes of a massive centenary celebration. Every city had something festive going on and every radio station was playing that catchy celebratory song, "One little two little three Canadians". Everyone was in a great mood ... and my parents had a plan.

They bought a camping trailer and enough supplies to last us six weeks. Then they packed all five kids into the station wagon, hitched up the trailer and headed eastward from the familiar comfort of our quiet West Hill street in Scarborough, Ontario to the vast unknown of this great land of ours. "We're going to see the country", they proclaimed patriotically and we set off on the journey of our young lifetimes.

Our first stop was Montreal. We wanted to see Expo '67 which was the Montreal World's Fair. We had relatives in the area so we met up with them and traveled together to the fair. There was so much to explore, but mostly I remember the rides at La Ronde. My mother told me that we lost my sister there at one point. We found her only because a friendly passer-by happened to put her on his shoulders and one of my cousins spotted her above the crowd. I don't remember this, but I'm sure some part of me was happy to see her again.

After Montreal, the plan was to head west as far as we could go. We traveled to Manitoba (I remember the mosquitoes) and then on to Saskatchewan (to visit my Aunt Julie), then through Alberta (we missed the Stampede, but we had a great time in Jasper) until finally we ended up in beautiful British Columbia. For me, this was the most memorable part of our journey. My memories of this province are like sensory snapshots in time.

I remember me and my four siblings gazing in awe at the majestic Rocky Mountains. I remember the exhilaration of throwing snowballs in July. But most of all, I remember touching clouds. On our way up the steep mountainside I could see the clouds hovering above us and I wondered what it was going to be like up there in the sky. I anticipated something heavenly, like little wispy angels with harps, like the ones I had seen during catechism class in our illustrated Bible. When we finally reached the lookout and we stepped out of the car it was ethereal. There was a quiet, dense fog everywhere and the sounds of our delighted squeals seemed muffled and amplified all at once. I remember thinking, "I'm in the clouds ... I'm touching the clouds!"

Later on that fall when we headed back to school I told all of my friends in Grade One that over my summer holiday I touched the clouds. No one believed me of course, but that only upset me a little. I knew I had been there and that was all that mattered to me. The experience was one that I would carry with me until this day. And now that I have written it down and I can read the words, I don't know how anyone could have doubted that it ever happened.

I remember touching the clouds... thanks Mom and Papa.

Kelly Stanutz-Sedlar, Intermediate Teacher

Un día entre las nubes

Para contarles mi recuerdo favorito, tengo que remontarme a mi niñez, hasta el verano de 1967. Tenía cinco años de edad (supongo que ahora se haya revelado mi edad presente) y Canadá estaba cumpliendo los 100 años. Ese verano, el país entero estaba en medio de una celebración centenaria masiva. En cada ciudad ocurría alguna fiesta y en cada estación de radio se oía esa canción celebratoria tan pegadiza, "One little two little three Canadians". Todo el mundo estaba de muy buen humor ... y mis padres tenían un plan.

Compraron un remolque de camping y provisiones suficientes para seis semanas. Embarcaron a los cinco niños en el coche, engancharon el remolque y, juntos, nos dirigimos hacia el este, fuera de la comodidad familiar de nuestra calle tranquila en Scarborough, Ontario, hacia lo desconocido enorme, de nuestro gran país. "Vamos a descubrir este país," proclamaron mis padres con gran orgullo y nos embarcamos en el viaje de nuestras vidas.

Nuestra primera parada fue la ciudad de Montreal. Queríamos ver el Expo '67, que fue la Feria Mundial de Montreal. Teníamos parientes en la región, así nos encontramos y viajamos juntos a la feria. Había tanto para explorar, pero por la mayor parte, me recuerdo del parque de atracciones que se llama "La Ronde" que hoy aun existe. Años después, mi madre me dijo que se perdió mi hermana en el parque ese día. La encontramos solamente porque un transeúnte simpático la llevó sobre sus hombros y una prima mía la reconoció. No me recuerdo en absoluto de esto (quizás porque mis padres decidieron ocultármelo, como una manera de protegerme de una profunda tristeza) pero imagino que yo estaba feliz de reunirme con ella.

Después de nuestra estancia en Montreal, el plan era de dirigirnos lo más al oeste posible. Viajamos a Manitoba (me recuerdo de los mosquitos, insectos inolvidables de toda excursión) luego a Saskatchewan (para visitar a mi tía Julia), a través de Alberta (faltamos al Stampede de Calgary, pero nos divertimos mucho en Jasper), hasta por fin, llegamos a la hermosa Columbia Británica. Para mí, esta parte del viaje fue la más memorable. Mis recuerdos de esta provincia son como fotografías sensoriales.

Recuerdo la mirada fija de mis cuatro hermanos al pie de las majestuosas Montañas Rocky. Recuerdo la alegría total que sólo se puede sentir tirando bolas de nieve en julio. Pero sobre todo, recuerdo tocar las nubes. Antes de nuestra subida por la montaña, se podían ver las nubes flotando con elegancia allí arriba . Me preguntaba cómo sería sentirse allí, en el cielo. Me imaginaba algo celestial, como pequeños ángeles menudos con arpas minúsculos, iguales a los que yo había visto en la Biblia durante mis clases de catecismo los domingos. Cuando llegamos finalmente a la cima de la montaña, la vista era etérea. Había una niebla densa y tranquila por todas partes y nuestra risa de alegría pareció apagada y ampliada a la vez. Recuerdo haber sentido dentro de mi ser, una extraordinaria experiencia y exclamé," ¡Estoy en medio de las nubes ...y puedo tocarlas!"

Más tarde, en el otoño, cuando regresamos a la escuela, les contaba a mis amiguitas en el primer grado que durante el verano toqué las nubes. Ellas no me creyeron, pero eso no me preocupaba porque esta linda experiencia la tuve junto con mi amada familia, fieles testigos de este hermoso y glorioso momento. Yo sabía que había tocado las nubes, y eso fue lo importante. La experiencia fue una que no iba a olvidar nunca. Y ahora que lo he escrito aquí y puedo leer las palabras claramente, me parece el cuento más creíble del mundo.

Recuerdo tocar las nubes ... muchas gracias Mamá y Papá.

Language : Spanish
Translated by : Kelly Stanutz-Sedlar, Intermediate Teacher

I remember

I will always remember the time I had no money to buy a present for my niece's birthday. When I did get money, I was supposed to buy clothes. When I got to the store I just knew I was forgetting something. I walked over to the little kids section in Toys R Us and I looked for something for about an hour, but still couldn't find anything for my niece. I was walking by one part of the store and I stopped and looked at this one stuffed animal. I decided this would be a great gift! It was about the same size as me, and I'm not the tallest person in the world.

When I was carrying it around the mall everyone was looking at me. It was very embarrassing, but I didn't really care because I knew that I was doing it for my niece, so it felt good. When I got home I put it on my bed and sprayed it with perfume so that it wouldn't smell bad from being in a store for so long.

The next day my sister came and picked me up. I took the stuffed animal, which was a pig, and we put it in the car. My sister couldn't see out the back window because of the stuffed pig. When we got to my sister's house, I pulled out the stuffed pig and walked in the door. My niece was nowhere to be found, so I just put it on the couch for whenever she would come downstairs from playing with all her friends. All the adults at the birthday party were in the dining room and so was I because I am considered one of the "adults". When I got back from the dining room the stuffed pig was gone, so I went upstairs to see where it was. I looked around the corner and there was the stuffed pig with my niece sleeping on it. It was a cute scene that I will probably always remember.

Josey Marion, Grade 8 Student

Yo Recuerdo

Siempre recordare el dia que no tenia dinero para comprarle un regalo a mi sobrina. Cuando me dieron el dinero, tenia que comprar ropa. Cuando llegue al almasen, sentia que se me habia olvidado algo. Camine a la section de niños y busque ropa por una hora, pero no encontre nada para mi Sobrina. Cuando caminaba por una parte del almasen vi un peluche vien bonito. Y decidi que era el mejor regalo! El peluche era de mi tamaño y yo no soy la persona mas alta del mundo.

Cuando llevava el peluche por el mall todos me miraban. Estaba bien apenada, pero no me importaba porque sabia que lo hacia por mi sobrina, entonses me senti bien. Cuando llegue a casa puse el peluche en mi cama y le puse perfume para que no hiediera de estar tanto tiempo en el mall.

El proximo dia mi hermana vino y me recohio. Aguare el peluche, que era un cuche y lo puse en el caro. Mi hermana no podia ver atras porque el peluche tapaba. Cuando llegamos a la casa de mi hermana, dentre por la puerta. No podiamos ayar mi sobrina, entonses puse el peluche en el sion para cuando bajara podriera jugar con el. Todos los adultos estab en la sala, y yo tambien porque yo soy considerada una "adulta". Cuando regrese al sion, el peluche no estaba, entonses fui ariba a buscarlo. Fui al cuarto de mi Sobrina y alli estaba el peluche com mi Sobrina durmiendo ensima del peluche. Era la escena mas agradable que nunca olvidare.

Language : Spanish
Translated by : Albert Alfaro, Grade 8 Student

Hawthorne *Writes*

because everyone has a story...

YOUR FUTURE IS NOW

25.   Swedish – Svenska

Swedish

There are just over 8 million people who speak Swedish in the world. Most of these people live in Sweden, however, Swedish is also spoken in neighbouring Finland and Norway. In fact, it is the second official language of Finland. Swedish is also spoken in Canada, Estonia, United Arab Emirates, and the United States.

Swedish is apart of the Indo-European family of languages. It is derived from the Donsk tunga or "Danish tongue" that was spoken in all of Scandinavia before the Middle Ages. The closest relatives to the Swedish language are Danish, Icelandic and Norwegian. As a result, Danes and Norwegians usually do not have difficulties communicating with Swedes.

Svenska

Det finns lite mer än 8 miljoner människor i världen som talar svenska. Dom flesta av dessa människorna bor i Sverige men dom talar även svenska i grannländerna Finnland och Norge. Svenska är faktiskt det andra officiella språket i Finnland. Svenska är också talat i Kanada, Estonien, Förenade Arab Emiraten och de Förenta Staterna.

Svenska skiljer sig från den Indo-Europeiska språk familjen. Det kommer utsprungligen från den Donsk tunga eller "Danska tungan" som talades i hela Skandinavien före medeltiden. Språken som är närmast svenska är danska, isländska och norska. Därför har danskar och norskar vanligtvis inga svårigheter att kommunisera med svenskar.

Language Description and Translation by: Marilyn Amey, Grade 4/5 Teacher, and Gunilla

My Grandmother

My grandparents came from an area that dates back 9000 years to the hunting culture of the Stone Age, and the reindeer herding culture of the 18th century. Norrbotten is the largest and most northerly province in Sweden. My grandmother, Helga Gustavsson, lived in the small village of Longvik. Strapping on her cross-country skis, she would travel over 20 kilometres to the village of Morjärv to take care of the Karlsson household where my grandfather lived with his 9 brothers, sister, father and ailing mother. The rest, as they say, is history; my grandfather married my grandmother in 1926 and soon after, they followed my grandfather's two brothers out to Vancouver, British Columbia to work in the lumber industry.

Of the nine Gustavsson children only my grandmother and her older sister, Lydia, immigrated to Canada. Like my grandfather's two brothers, they came with little money but huge dreams for a quality of life that would surpass that of their homeland. Having arrived in Halifax harbour with no money to continue their voyage to Vancouver, they sold icecream, and saved enough to pay for the Immigrant Train out west.

Adjusting to their new life in Vancouver was initially hard for my grandparents, but in the company of my grandfather's brothers, they would rekindle stories of their youth in Sweden, and stoke the fire of their cultural traditions. In time, they called Vancouver home, and raised two daughters who would teach them the language that would lead to opportunities that embraced their dreams. News from Sweden was confined to mail. Good news, like Emelia's (my grandmother's sister) marriage, nurtured the homesick heart. Letters followed announcing the births of Emelia's three daughters: Britt, Elsie, and Clary. Then, a letter arrived explaining that Emelia had died of tuberculosis. For years later, my grandmother wondered what happened to her nieces, Emelia's daughters.

Like a knife to butter, time slides by. My grandparents' daughters grew up, got married and had children. Relentless in its pursuit to forge ahead, time carries us through all events despite our reluctance.

My grandmother was a pillar for her 91 years. With her passing, we knew that our sense of who we were and where we came from was now relegated to memory.

Soon after my grandmother's death, my parents trekked to the north of Sweden. While visiting the city of Luleå, they went into a quaint shop to look for a souvenir. A conversation soon developed between the sales clerk and my mother. Upon hearing where my parents live, the lady began to smile with the revelation that they had something in common. The woman explained that she had two aunts who had moved to Canada a very long time ago. She said their names were Helga and Lydia. Now it was my mother's turn to smile for before her stood Elsie, Emelia's daughter.

I like to think my grandmother was there that day. She would have been found behind the knowing smile, in the joy of tears, and felt in the warmth of the embrace. In my mind's eye, I see her there with her sister, Emelia. They would have lingered with their daughters into the evening when Elsie introduced my parents to her older sister, Britt. As the puzzle pieces gave way to the picture, I imagine my grandmother and her sister looking on.

Marilyn Amey, Grade 4/5 Teacher

Min Mormor

Mina morforaldrar kom fran ett omrade daterat 9000 ar sedan, till stenalderns jakt kultur och 1700-talets ren kultur. Norrbotten ar det storsta och nordligaste lanet i Sverige. For manga manniskor som bor dar representerar Norrbotten Europas sista vilda naturomrade, men med den vaxande industrin ar det svart att bevara dess naturliga skonhet.

Min mormor, Helga Gustavsson, bodde i en liten by som heter Longvik. Pa sina skidor akte hon mer an 20 kilometer till byn Morjarv for att skota om familjen Karlsson dar min morfar bodde med sina 10 broder, syster, pappa och sjuka mamma. Vad som hande sen ar som dom sager historia; min morfar och mormor gifte sig 1926 och ett ar senare foljde dom min morfars tva broder till Vancouver, British Columbia for att arbeta i virkes industrin.

Av Gustavsson barnen, och det var 9 av dom, var det bara min mormor och hennes aldre syster Lydia som immigrerade till Kanada. Liksom min mofars tva broder kom dom med lite pengar men med stora drommar om en livskvalitet hogre an i deras hemland. Nar dom anlande i hamnen i Halifax utan pengar for resten av resan till Vancouver salde dom nagot som var obekant till dom, glass, och kunde slutligen ta Immigrations taget vasterut.

Det var svart for mina morfaraldrar att vanja sig vid sitt nya liv i Vancouver utan nagon kunskap av det engelska spraket. Dom bode nara min morfars broder, pratade ofta om sin ungdom i Sverige och uppeholl sina svenska kulturella traditioner. Sa smaningom kallade dom Vancouver sitt hem och uppfostrade tva dottrar som larde dem spraket, vilket i tur lat dem leva i den stil dom hade dromt om. Men deras nya hem var langt fran Sverige och det var inte mojligt att aka och halsa pa. Min mormors systrar och broder var alltid i hennes tankar. Nyheter fran Sverige kom med posten, och en av Helgas systrar, Emelia, gifte sej strax efter Helga hade flyttat till Vancouver. Efter ett tag horde mim mormor att Emelia hade tre barn, Clary, Elsie och Britt. Sorgliga nyheter foljde om att Emelia var sjuk med tuberkulos och kunde inte ta hand om sin barn. Darfor blev dom bortgivna till en annan familj. Emelia dog en kort tid senare. For manga ar efter det undrade min mormor vad det hade blivit av hennes systerdottrar.

Som en kniv genom smor glider tiden vidare. Min mormors dottrar vaxte upp, gifte sej och hade egna barn. Jag har kommit att forsta att tiden ar bade van och fiende. En del saker, som speciella tillfallen, andrar sej aldrig, till exempel min morfar och hans broder som kladde ut sej till jultomten och halsade pa mej och min syster pa julafton. Smorgasbord med min mormors brad, sill och gravad lax och gamla svenska sanger mina slaktingar brukade sjunga sa hogt att det var nastan otalbart, ar minnen som jag fortfarande har kvar. Tiden tar dem vi alskar, som min morfar som dog nar jag var bara 6 ar gammal. Vi hade tur att min mormors tid kom mycket senare. Vid den tiden bodde jag i Ottawa. Jag kommer ihag den dagen hon dog. Mina foraldrar hade precis kommit tillbaka till Vancouver efter att ha halsat pa mej. Istallet for deras vanliga telefon samtal om att dom hade landat ordentligt och for att tacka mej, igen, for deras resa, gav dom meddelande att min mormor hade dott. Hon var en pelare under hennes 91 ar och vi visste att vara kanslor om vem vi ar och var vi kom fran, var nu en del av varan personliga historia.

Kanske var det mim mormors dod som gjorde att mina foraldrar tog sin forsta resa till Sverige. Jag ar inte saker, men mindre an ett ar senare akte dom till norra Sverige for att se staden Lulea i Norrbottens lan. Slaktingar, glada att se sina avlagsna familje- medlemmar fran Kanada, visade min mamma och pappa byn dar min mammas foraldrar vaxte upp. Efter en dag av 'sightseeing' gick mina foraldrar in i en liten affar i Lulea. Min mamma gick for att betala for nagra sma tavlor som hon senare gav till min syster och mej. Som hon hade gjort manga ganger denna resan, bad hon om ursakt till expediten for att hon var sa dalig pa det svenska spraket. Nyfiken fragade damen var min mamma bodde. Nar hon svarade Vancouver, British Columbia blev damens ogon stora och hon log och sa att dom hade nagot gemensamt. Kvinnan forklarade att hon hade tva mostrar som flyttade till Kanada for mycket lange sedan. Dom hade tagit ett tag till Vancouver dar dom bodde resten av sina liv. Hon sa att deras namn var Helga och Lydia. Nu var det min mammas tur att le. Efter en lang kram och manga tarar blev det uppklarat att expeditens namn var Elsie och att hennes mammas namn var Emelia.

Jag tror att min mormor maste ha varit dar den dagen. Hon syndes i de upplysta leendena, i dom gladjefyllda tararna, och hon kandes i kramarnas varme. Och hon var dar med sin syster, Emelia. Dom stannade med sina dottrar genom kvallen nar Elsie presenterade mina foraldrar till sin andra syster, Britt, som var pa vag att aka hem till Kalifornien nasta dag. Min mormor och hennes syster tittade pa nar pussel bitarna formade bilden.

Language : Swedish
Translated by : Gunilla

Hawthorne *Writes*
because everyone has a story...

YOUR FUTURE IS NOW

26. Turkish – Türkçe

Turkish is spoken by an estimated 50 million people. It is spoken throughout Turkey, as well as in Bulgaria, Cyprus, Greece, and Uzbekistan.

My bike

My mom got me a present. It was a bike. The bike was red. The bike was pretty. I was happy because it was beautiful. The bike was fast.

Seda Hashim Hasan, Grade 1 Student

Benim anem bene hediye aldi. Benim hediyem bisikletidi. Benim bisikletim girmizi. Cok guzel. Ben cok sevdim iste benim bisikletim cok guzel. Benim bisikletim cok hizlii

Language: Turkish
Translated by: Semer Hashim Hasan, Grade 8 Student

Hawthorne *Writes*
because everyone has a story...

27.   Urdu – اردو

Urdu

Urdu is the national language of Pakistan. More than 220 million people in sub-continent regard it as their mother tongue and it is actively used by 400 million people in Pakistan and India in their daily life at work & home. Outside the sub-continent large Urdu speaking communities are in USA, UK, Mauritius, South Africa, Yemen, Uganda, Singapore, Nepal, New Zealand & Germany.

The language Urdu is a mixture of a few other languages like Turkish, Farsi, Arabic & English. The word Urdu itself is a Turkish word which means "An army" which give the general idea of a big group of something. The script of Urdu language is the same as for Arabic and is also written from right to left. Mostly newspapers, books and general material is printed in the most popular script known as "Nastaliq." The other script in use is known as "Nasakh.". Urdu has 34 letters in the alphabet.

اردو

اردو پاکستان کی قومی زبان ہے۔ 220 ملین لوگ برصغیر میں اسے اپنی مادری زبان
سمجھتے ہیں اور 400 ملین لوگ پاکستان اور انڈیا
میں اسے روزمرہ زندگی میں اپنے گھر اور دفاتر میں استعمال کرتے
ہیں۔ برصغیر کے باہر اردو بولنے والے لوگ امریکہ، برطانیہ ، موریشینس ، جنوبی
افریقہ ، یمن ، یوگینڈا ، سنگاپور ، نیپال ، نیوزی لینڈ اور جرمنی میں رہتے ہیں ۔
اردو زبان دوسری کئ زبانوں سے متاثر ہے۔ اس میں ترکی ، فارسی،
عربی اور انگریزی زبان کے الفاظ پائے جاتے ہیں۔ لفظ اردو خود   ترکی زبان
سے ہے۔ جسکا مطلب ' فوج ' ہے۔ اردو طرز تحریر اور عربی طرز تحریر ایک ہی
طرح کی ہیں.اور سیدھے ہاتھ سے الٹے ہاتھ کو لکھی جاتی ہے۔ اخبار اور کتابیں '
نستالیق' طرز تحریر میں چھپتے ہیں جبکہ دوسرے طرز تحریر کا نام ' نسخ' ہے۔ اردو
زبان مین 34 حروف ہیں.

Language Description and Translation by: Tamkeen Pirzada

The Dreadful Earthquake

Last year I went on a vacation to Pakistan. One night I was sleeping genially in my bedroom and had no concept of what was about to occur. Next morning I woke up because my parents were calling my brother & me. When I sat up I was feeling very dizzy. My bed was shaking from right to left, my mirror, chairs and everything was shaking. I looked at my fan; it looked as if it were to fall. My mom quickly came up and grabbed my brother, and me and we went downstairs. Our granny was with us. We went outside quickly, the earthquake was about 5 minutes long. We thought it was just a normal one, it was quite strong, but it came and went.

When we came back into the house I turned on the TV and quickly ran to sit on the staircase (it was near the door that heads out-side). What we saw was horrible. There was news on every channel. News from other cities & international countries.

The magnitude on the Richter scale was 7.6.

We were living in Islamabad, which is the capital of Pakistan. There are a lot of high-rise buildings & apartments. There was one building "The Margala Towers". One of the blocks of the tower collapsed to the ground. Other buildings such as schools & colleges were seriously damaged. Many residential areas were damaged also.

People came onto the roads and refused to go back home. People were so scared & no matter what, they stayed outside. Other areas and cities were completely destroyed, like Kashmir, Bala Coat, Ravla Coat, Muzafarabad, & many more hill stations as well. There was absolutely nothing left in those areas, just wrecked or broken houses, and homes with a broken roof on the ground in which they slept and kept away from the cold.

My family & especially me were very scared. Because our rooms were upstairs, my parents, my brother and I slept in the living room. I didn't agree to go up and sleep in our rooms so my family kept me company downstairs. For many days we kept sleeping in the living room,

because we felt a lot of aftershocks during the day and evening. When we went to sleep the first night, the lights went and it started to rain.

Whenever we went to sleep, I thought about the "Margala Towers", the dust of the cement, the red dust clouds of the cement, & about the people who were suffering, the rain, thunder, and the coldness. It must have been a hundred times scarier for them than it was for me.

The government of Pakistan along with the rest of the world is working day & night on the rehabilitation work in the affected areas.

Now I am in Canada & I am sure the next time I go visit Pakistan I'll see it in good condition just as it was before "THE DREADFUL EARTHQUAKE"

Duaa Inam, Grade 4/5 Student

خَوفناک زلزلہ

پچھلے سال میں چھٹیوں میں پاکستان گئی تھی ۔ ایک رات میں سکون سے اپنے کمرے میں سو رہی تھی اور مجھے کچھ اندازہ نہ تھا کہ کیا ہونے والا ہے۔ اگلی صبح میں اپنے والدین کی آواز پر اٹھی جو مجھے اور میرے بھائی کو بلا رہے تھے۔ جب میں اٹھی تو مجھے بے سکونی محسوس ہوئ. میرا پلنگ دائیں بائیں ہل رہا تھا. میرا آئینہ ، کرسیاں اور سب کچھ ہل رہا تھا ۔ میں نے پنکھے کی طرف دیکھا تو مجھے لگا کہ وہ گر جائے گا۔ میری امی جلدی آئیں اور مجھے اور میرے بھائی کو بازو سے پکڑ کر نیچے لے گئیں. ہماری دادی جان بھی ہمارے ساتھ تھیں۔ ہم جلدی سے گھر سے باہر چلے گئے. زلزلہ کا دورانیہ پانچ منٹ تھا۔ زلزلہ اگرچہ شدید تھا مگر یہ ہی سمجھے کہ ایک نارمل زلزلہ ہے ۔ جو آیا اور چلا گیا.

ریکٹر سکیل پر زلزلے کی شدد 7.6 تھی۔

جب ہم گھر میں واپس آئے تو میں نے ٹی وی اور جلدی سے قریب ہی بیٹھ گئ. ٹی وی پر جو کچھ ہم نے دیکھا وہ بہت خوفناک تھا۔ ہر چینل پر تمام ملک اور انٹرنیشنل ممالک سے خبریں جاری تھیں۔

ہم اسلام آباد میں رہ رہے تھے۔ جو کہ پاکستان کا دارُلخلافہ ہے۔ وہاں بے شمار بلند عمارتیں اور اپارٹمنٹس ہیں۔ 'مارگلہ ٹاورز' کے نام سے کچھ اپارٹمنٹن بلاک ہیں۔ ان میں سے ایک بلاک بلکل تباہ ہو گیا.اور کی سکولوں اور کالجوں کی عمارتوں کو بھی نقصان پہنچا. رہائشی علاقے بھی کافی متائثر ہوئے۔

لوگ سڑکوں پر نکل آئے اور اُنے گھر واپس جانا نہیں چاہتے تھے کیونکہ سب بہت زیادہ ڈرے ہوئے تھے۔ مُلک کے دوسرے شہر جیسے کشمیر ، بالا کوٹ، راولاکوٹ، مظفرآباد اور دوسرے پہاڑی علاقے مکمل طور پر تباہ ہو گئے۔ ان علاقوں میں تباہ شدہ گھروں کے علاوہ کچھ نہ بچا تھا. ٹوٹی ہوئ چھتوں کے ساتھ شدید سردی میں وہ وہیں رہ رہے تھے اور ان ہی گھروں میں سو رہے تھے۔

میری فیملی اور خاص طور پر میں بہت زیادہ خوفزدہ تھی۔ ہمارے بیڈرومز اوپر کی منزل پر تھے۔ مگر میرے والدین میں اور میرا بھائی نیچے ' لونگ روم' میں سوئے۔ میں اوپر جا کر اپنے کمرے میں سونے کے لئے بالکل تیار نہ تھی۔ اس لیے میری فیملی نے میرا پورا ساتھ دیا اور نیچے کی منزل پر ہی رکھا۔ اس دوران ہمیں دن اور رات کے دورانیے میں زلزلے کے مزید جھٹکے محسوس ہوتے رہے۔ میں جب بھی سونے لگتی مجھے تباہ شدہ مارگلا ٹاور ، اسکے سیمنٹ کا دھواں ، سیمنٹ سے اٹھتے سرخ مٹی کے بادل اور وہ سب لوگ یاد آتے جو بارش ، بادلوں کی گرج اور شدید سردی برداشت کر رہے تھے۔ ان کا خوف میرے خوف سے کئ گنا زیادہ تھا۔

اب پاکستان کی حکومت دنیا کے دوسرے ممالک کے ساتھ مل کر متاثرہ علاقوں میں
تعمیرِ نو کا کام کر رہی ہے۔

اب میں کینیڈا میں ہوں اور میں اُمید کرتی ہوں کہ جب میں دوبارہ پاکستان جاوں گی تو
پاکستان کو پہلے کی طرح اچھی حالت میں دیکھوں گی. جیسا وہ اس خوفناک زلزلے
سے پہلے تھا۔

Language: Urdu
Translated by: Bushra Gulzar

Ciao Arabia, Hello Canada

On a late sunny afternoon in 2003, my parents were thinking about my sister's university education. We were currently living in Saudi Arabia, and the universities over there weren't as good as you might have thought. My parents decided to move to a new place: Canada. Our family kept getting warnings from friends that stated that everything in Canada was expensive and there were lots of taxes. We will discuss that later in the story.

On the 10th of July, we left for Canada and took a flight to London. From there, me and my family flew to Ottawa, not knowing what was to come.

When we first decided to move, my sister had applied to different universities across Canada. She had qualified for most universities but chose the University of Ottawa for her future education. Now she is a second year student of Commerce. In 2005 my elder brother also went to U Ottawa and entered the Faculty of Science.

Having reached Ottawa, we waited for our luggage to arrive, and surprisingly, it got collected rather quickly. Next, we called a cab to get to the townhouse we had previously rented. When the moving company arrived, they handed us all the stuff we had shipped, only to find that my mom's glassware had been smashed because of the way the boxes had been 'thrown around' by the moving company.

As I told you earlier in the story, people warned us of high taxes and other financial problems. We soon discovered that they were wrong. As we started to grocery shop and buy things, we found out that everything was fair priced and you cold shop online too! You couldn't do these things in Saudi Arabia. Nor were there any movie theatres there. Canada has it all!

School was first. My parents signed me up with the OCDSB (Ottawa-Carleton District School Board). I went to Adult High School take an admission test. A kind and gentle Chinese lady offered me the test

papers. The good thing was I got admitted into Hawthorne School which was pretty close to my house.

It was my first day of school. I had been put in Ms. Menzies' class. I made two new friends: Tanzim and Alaa. Alaa comes from Lebanon, in the Middle East. Tanzim comes from Bangladesh, a small country to the east of India.

Then December came along. It started to snow exactly on the 1st of December. This was my first experience with a winter since Saudi Arabia is a dry and humid country. It never snows and is always hard and rocky.

I've moved to a higher grade now in Mrs. Amey's class, and so far I've been enjoying myself. I even got my computer experience from Canada thanks to the computer I have in my basement. I hope you enjoyed my story of coming to Canada.

Ismail Pirzada, Grade 4 Student

الوداع عربیہ ، سلام کینیڈا

2003 میں میرے والدین اور ہم بہن بھائی سعودی عرب میں رہ رہے تھے۔ اُن دنوں میرے والدین میری بڑی بہن کی یونیورسٹی تعلیم کے لئے سوچ رہے تھے۔ سعودی عرب میں کے یونیورسٹیاں تو بہت ہیں لیکن اونچے معیار کی نہیں۔ چنانچہ کینیڈا آنے کے بارے میں کے فیصلہ ہوا۔ لوگوں نے ہمیں بہت ڈرایا کہ کینیڈا میں بہت مہنگائی ہے ، اور ٹیکس بھی بہت دینا پڑے گا۔ان سب باتوں کے بارے میں ،میں آگے چل کر آپ کو بتاوں گا۔

آخر 10 جولائ 2004 کو ہم کینیڈا کیلئے روانہ ہونے،یہ نہ جانتے ہونے کہ آگے کیا ہونے والا ہے۔ راستے میں ہم لندن رکے اور ہماری منزل 'اوٹاوا' تھی۔ یہاں آنے سے پہلے میری بہن نے بہت یونیورسٹیوں میں داخلے کیلئے درخواستیں دیں تھیں اور سبھی نے انکو داخلہ دے بھی دیا تھا، لیکن میری بہن نے ' یونیورسٹی آف اوٹاوا' کو اپنی آئندہ تعلیم کے لئے چنا۔ اب وہ 'کامرس' کے دوسرے سال میں ہیں اور 2005 میں میرے بڑے بھائی نے بھی اسی یونیورسٹی میں سائنس کے شعبے میں داخلہ لیا۔

جب ہم اوٹاوا پہنچے تو ہوائ اڈے پر ہمارا سامان جلد ہی آگیا اور ہم ٹیکسی لے کر اس گھر کی طرف چل پڑے جو میرے ابو نے پہلے ہی لے رکھا تھا۔ کچھ دنوں بعد ہمارا وہ سامان پہنچا جو ہم نے بحری جہاز کے ذریعے منگوایا تھا۔ لیکن میری امی کو یہ دیکھ کر بہت افسوس ہوا کہ شیشے کا سامان ٹوٹا ہوا ہے۔ یہ غلطی اس کمپنی کی تھی جس نے سامان ہمارے گھر تک پہنچایا تھا۔

جیسا کہ میں نے آپ کو کہانی کے شروع میں بتایا تھا کہ لوگوں نے ہمیں یہاں کے حالات کے بارے میں ڈرایا تھا۔ لیکن ہمیں جلد ہی اس بات کا اندازاہ ہوا کہ وہ لوگ غلط تھے۔ جیسے جیسے ہم نے گھریلو استعمال کی چیزیں خریدنا شروع کیں تو معلوم ہوا کہ سب چیزوں کی قیمتیں مناسب ہیں۔اور ہم انٹرنٹ کے ذریعے بھی خریداری کر سکتے ہیں۔ ایسا سعودی عرب میں ممکن نہ تھا۔ وہاں سینما گھر بھی نہ تھے ۔ کینیڈا میں سب کچھ ہے۔

یہاں آنے کے بعد سب سے پہلے سکول کی باری تھی۔ مجھے سکول میں داخلے کے لئے امتحان دینا پڑا جو ایک بڑے لوگوں کے سکول میں ہوا۔ وہاں پر ایک بہت ہی نرم دل اور مہربان چینی خاتون نے میرا امتحان لیا۔ سب سے اچھی بات یہ ہوئ کہ مجھے Hawthorne سکول میں داخلہ ملا جو میرے گھر کے قریب ہی ہے۔

یہ میرا سکول میں پہلا دن تھا اور میں 'Ms.Menzies' کی کلاس میں گیا۔ یہاں میں نے دو نئے دوست بنائے۔ ایک 'Tanzim'، جسکا تعلق بنگلادیش سے ہے۔ بنگلادیش ہندوستان کے شمال میں ایک چھوٹا سا ملک ہے۔ دوسرا دوست لبنان سے ہے جسکا نام 'Alaa' ہے۔ لبنان مشرقِ وسطیٰ میں ہے۔

کچھ ہی عرصے بعد دسمبر کا مہینہ شروع ہو گیا اور پہلی ہی دسمبر کو خوب برف
باری ہوئ. سعودی عرب سے آنے کے بعد یہ میری پہلی برف باری تھی۔ کیونکہ
سعودی عرب تو ایک گرم ملک ہے۔ جہاں کبھی برف باری نہیں ہوتی۔

اب میں اگلی کلاس میں چلا گیا ہوں. جو 'Mrs.Amey ' کی کلاس ہے۔ ابھی تک تو
مجھے بہت اچھا لگ رہا ہے۔ میں نے کینیڈا آکر بہت کچھ سیکھا ہے۔ جسمیں کمپیئوٹر
بھی شامل ہے۔

امید ہے آپکو میرے کینیڈا آنے کی کہانی پسند آنے گی.

Language: Urdu
Translated by: Tamkeen Pirzada

My Family

My baby sister's name is Mariam. She is three months old. I like to play with her and hold her. I also like to play with my Barbies and have a tea party with them. I love to go to my Grandfather and Grandmother's house. I don't like it when my Grandmother I sick. With my Grandfather, I sometimes go to the river to feed the ducks, the seagulls, the groundhogs and the squirrels. My family is a great thing to have.

Sahar Naveed, Kindergarten Student

میری چھوٹی بہن کا نام مریم ہے اور وہ تین ماہ کی ہے ۔
مجھے اسکو گود میں اٹھانا اور اسکے ساتھ کھیلنا بہت
اچھا لگتا ہے ۔
اس کے علاوہ میں اپنی باربی کی گڑیا کے ساتھ کھیلتی ہوں
اور ان کے ساتھ چائے کی دعوت کرتی ہوں ۔
میں اپنے نانا اور نانی جان کے گھر بہت شوق سے جاتی ہوں ۔
مجھے اچھا نہیں لگتا جب میری نانی جان بیمار ہوتی ہیں ۔
میں اپنے ناناجان کے ساتھ کبھی کبھار دریا کے کنارے
ٹہرتی بھی ہوں ، بطخوں ، گلہریوں اور کبوتروں کا کھانا کھلانے جاتی
ہوں ۔   میں اپنے خاندان کو پا کر بہت خوش ہوں ۔ (ختم شد)

Language : Urdu
Translated by : ???

Snakes

A boa is strong because it has big teeth. It eats other animals. I have never seen a boa. My grandma told me about a boa. It went into her house. I wish I had seen it myself. Snakes are my favourite animal.

Naseem Mahamed, Grade 1 Student

Language: Urdu
Translated by: Tamkeen Pirzada

Hawthorne *Writes*
because everyone has a story...

YOUR FUTURE IS NOW

28. Yiddish

Yiddish is spoken by an estimated 50 thousand people in Germany. It is also spoken in Belgium, France, Israel, Netherlands, and Sweden, to name a few countries.

My Family Treasure

My family treasure is a charm bracelet that has been passed down from my great-grandmother Alice Anzarut. She made this charm bracelet in the throughout the 30's and 40's. At that time her family was living in Alexandria in Egypt. There are few charms I know the story of on this bracelet because unfortunately I never got to meet her. The charm bracelet is made of 24 karat gold and all but 2 charms are made out of gold as well. There are 23 charms on the bracelet and almost all of the charms move or open up. Here are a few of the charms stories. One of the charms is a golden tank. When my great-grandmother lived in Egypt her husband served in the British navy. Alice always enjoyed having charms from all over the world and so my great-grandfather brought her back, from one of his breaks a golden tank. Another one of my favorites is a book, the on the cover says you and me in french. As an anniversary gift My great-grandfather, Ben Anzarut, bought her this little book and had their names inscribed on the first page and their wedding date. The other pages have the names f their children including my grandmother. A few more of my favorite charms are two golden tablets which are inscribed in Hebrew with the Ten Commandments, an ivory scarab, an old fashioned record player, and a horse and carriage.

My great-grandmother wore the charm bracelet every day and she even wore it on the plane over to Canada. It was then passed down to my grandmother who passed it down to my mother, and it will soon be passed down to my sister or I. I always regret not being able to meet my great-grandmother but from what I hear I would have liked her.

Jessica Ostroff, Grade 7 Student

Language: Yiddish
Translated by: Gerry Ostroff

About the Project Coordinators

Mike Fuchigami

Mike Fuchigami is new to the classroom, but not new to education. He has spent several years working overseas in education and international development in Australia, Thailand, Zambia, Israel and the Palestinian territories. This is his second year of surviving and thriving in the classroom.

Susan Newton

Susan Newton is an experienced teacher with OCDSB, who is committed to advocating for children and families The love and support of her friends and famliy Bryan, Rachael and Katrina make all of this possible.

Francesse Kopczewski

Francesse Kopczewski is the principal at Hawthorne Public School.

Permissions

Read our stories online at:
www1.ocdsb.ca/HawtWeb/HawthorneWrites